*A Physician Explains
Ellen White's Counsel on*

DRUGS, HERBS, AND NATURAL REMEDIES

To order additional copies of *A Physician Explains Ellen White's Counsel on Drugs, Herbs, and Natural Remedies,* call 1-800-765-6955.

Visit us at www.reviewandherald.com for information on other Review and Herald products.

A Physician Explains
Ellen White's Counsel on

DRUGS, HERBS, AND NATURAL REMEDIES

Mervyn G. Hardinge, M.D., Dr.P.H., Ph.D.

REVIEW AND HERALD® PUBLISHING ASSOCIATION
HAGERSTOWN, MD 21740

This book was
Edited by Gerald Wheeler
Copyedited by Jocelyn Fay and James Cavil
Designed by Mark O'Connor
Cover design by Mark O'Connor
Cover photos: Joel Springer, Corbis Images, PhotoDisc
Typeset: 11/14 Palatino

PRINTED IN U.S.A.

05 04 03 02 01   5 4 3 2 1

R&H Cataloging Service
Hardinge, Mervyn Gilbert, 1914-
    A physician explains Ellen White's counsel on drugs, herbs, and natural remedies.

    1. Drugs.   2. Herbs.   3. Medical botany.   4. Health.
5. Medicine—History.   I. Title.

                        615.1

ISBN 0-8280-1557-0

This book is dedicated to the Great Physician,
who has all wisdom and understanding.

CONTENTS

ABBREVIATIONS

BCL   *Battle Creek Letters*
CD   *Counsels on Diet and Foods*
CG   *Child Guidance*
CH   *Counsels on Health*
CT   *Counsels to Parents, Teachers, and Students*
DA   *The Desire of Ages*
EGW Ellen G. White
Ev   *Evangelism*
HL   *Healthful Living*
LLM *Loma Linda Messages*
MH   *The Ministry of Healing*
MM   *Medical Ministry*
1MR Ellen G. White, *Manuscript Releases*, vol. 1 (2MR, etc., for vols. 2-21)
PC   *Paulson Collection of Ellen G. White Letters*
RH   *Review and Herald*
1SG *Spiritual Gifts*, vol. 1 (2SG, etc., for vols. 2-4)
1SM *Selected Messages*, book 1 (2SM, etc., for books 2, 3)
SpM *Spalding and Magan's Unpublished Manuscript Testimonies of Ellen G. White*
1T   *Testimonies for the Church*, vol. 1 (2T, etc., for vols. 2-9)
Te   *Temperance*

FOREWORD

An estimated one third of the world's population suffers physically, mentally, or emotionally at any given time. Notwithstanding the amazing advancement of medical and surgical science, sickness and disease remain rampant. Dr. Hardinge's book offers a scientific and practical analysis of the predicament we face. It is not only intensely interesting but informative. With many new drugs emerging each year, with names that are difficult even to pronounce, you will agree that the book is timely. It clearly documents why we desperately need health education and lifestyle changes today. In spite of regulations and sincere efforts on the part of physicians, government agencies, and pharmaceutical companies, we periodically hear reports that even approved medications have to be withdrawn from the market. Sick people are often impatient and in a hurry to get well, and as a result they become easy victims of beguiling advertising for some new wonder drug.

Our world is learning that we must give priority to preventive medicine. We should develop greater appreciation for the amazing restorative powers of nature—exercise, rest, fresh air, water, and sunshine.

Some of you might be asking, "Who is Ellen G. White?" She was born in New England and enjoyed a long and productive life. Along with her husband, James, and Joseph Bates, a retired sea captain, they cofounded one of the world's fastest growing churches. As a result of about 2,000 dreams, visions, and revelations that she, and others, believed came from God, she wrote on a wide range of topics covering the life of Jesus Christ, nutrition, health, educational theory, marriage, the home and family, and spiritual nurture. She had only limited formal schooling, yet when she died at age 87 she left more than 100,000 pages of literary productions. Ellen White is the world's most translated woman and the most translated American writer of either sex. Paul Harvey, the popular American Broadcasting Company news commentator and United Features syndicated columnist, stated: "Ellen White wrote with such profound understanding on the subject of nutrition that all but two of the many principles she espoused have been scientifically established."

Many well-informed people seem to know little or nothing about her, yet Edith Deen in *Great Women of the Christian Faith* called her "a spokesman for God." William Foxwell Albright was America's and perhaps one of the world's foremost archaeologists during the twentieth century. He wrote more than 800 publications on archaeology, the Bible, and ancient Near Eastern subjects. Albright investigated the life and claims of Ellen White in his book *From the Stone Age to Christianity,* naming her as one of the five individuals whom he considered to be authentic "prophets" during the past 250 years. If some of her counsel regarding drugs, herbs, and healthful living sounds a bit extreme today, imagine how it must have seemed at the beginning of the twentieth century. Yet modern science continues more and more to say that she was right. Ellen White placed great emphasis on wellness and health rather than sickness. The great challenge is to keep people in good health rather than trying to nurse them back from sickness.

My friend, you hold in your hands a truly fascinating book about a major contemporary issue. Read it, and you will be glad you did.   *Neal C. Wilson*

S eventh-day Adventists have been inordinately privileged to have available to them divinely inspired counsels regarding healthful living, conveyed through the many writings of Ellen G. White. Scientific research has continually confirmed and supported many of their inspired concepts and principles. Some of this data has come from Seventh-day Adventists themselves as they have received significant health benefits from following the lifestyle Mrs. White recommended.

During the nineteenth century, when Ellen White received her health counsels, medicine commonly used poisonous drugs. She constantly urged people to avoid such agents as far as possible. Many Seventh-day Adventists and others have followed her advice, just as they did her leading in the dietary realm. In the twentieth century, as the science of pharmacology advanced, medical science developed many drugs that were much less toxic than those employed during the previous century. They have received widespread use and saved countless lives. Seventh-day Adventists have had to struggle with the question of how to relate to such medications.

I know of no one more qualified to address this issue than the author of this book, Mervyn G. Hardinge, M.D., Dr.P.H., Ph.D. As a longtime academic associate and personal friend of Dr. Hardinge, I can testify to his strong commitment to the inspiration of the health writings of Ellen G. White. I can also speak of his scientific expertise and objectivity, having collaborated with him both on research projects and in the classroom. In addition to his M.D. degree from Loma Linda University, Dr. Hardinge has received doctoral research level education in both nutrition and pharmacology from leading scientists at Harvard University and Stanford University. His deep commitment to the inspiration of Ellen G. White and his scientific background give him a unique ability to address the topics of this book.

In my view, this book provides a remarkably thorough and objective analysis of Ellen White's comments on the use of medical drugs. Dr. Hardinge has carefully researched the nature and scope of drug therapy in use during the period she received her inspired counsel. Then, in a historical tour de force, he systematically considers her comments and places them in their historical context. Further, he forthrightly addresses in a balanced manner their relationship to the status and nature of drug therapy in the twenty-first century. Hardinge also deals with the current exploding usage of herbal remedies, analyzing them in the context of Ellen White's counsels on "natural" remedies. In addition, Dr. Hardinge addresses her own use of drugs from the perspective of her inspired statements.

Dr. Hardinge has done a great service to all Seventh-day Adventists and others aware of Ellen White's work in producing this comprehensive examination of her counsels on medications and health. I strongly commend the book as the "final" word on the topic of Ellen White and medications.

Ian M. Fraser, Ph.D.
Distinguished Emeritus
Professor of Pharmacology
School of Medicine
Loma Linda University

I n this book Mervyn Hardinge provides an answer to a major question that has perplexed many Seventh-day Adventists for nearly 100 years. The question is: What should be our understanding of the role of drug medication in treating the sick, given the pointed counsels Ellen White makes against such use?
Some are uneasy if they take medicines and are uneasy if they don't! Others are comfortable with and have benefited from employing various medications, and so have decided that Ellen White was wrong in condemning drug medication.

Still others take her advice very literally and have abandoned the use of modern medicines. Such individuals are very sincere and devout. They often lean toward alternate medicine and embrace a variety of herbal remedies that are really "folk medicines" and are as yet untested. Also such people claim to be the true followers of Ellen White's counsels.

While much has been written through the years in this highly controversial issue, Hardinge has researched the subject from a historical and scientific basis. This book shows that a correct understanding comes only when we seek what Ellen White really meant by the words she used, and when we recognize the way physicians practiced medicine in her time.

While at times Ellen White recommended the use of an herbal remedy, what she had in mind is a far cry from what goes under that label today. Hardinge points out the complex nature of the mixtures of herbs and medicinal plants sold in health food stores. Each plant or herb often consists of a thousand or more chemicals, hundreds having biological activity. Combining multiple ingredients from many different sources in one capsule produces a very complex medication. It is no longer a simple remedy. Such multiingredient capsules escape supervision by the Food and Drug Administration, because they sell as "food supplements." They are not standardized; nor have they been tested for efficacy or toxicity. The manufacturers carefully avoid specific therapeutic claims; instead they make vague general statements about their products supporting the immune system or prostate health or acting as memory "enhancers" or similar nonspecific statements.

Dr. Hardinge is eminently qualified to probe the subject. A deeply religious man, he has always made God's will for his life his first concern. On the scientific side he is doubtless one of the most highly educated in the church today. He holds three earned doctorate degrees and two master's degrees from prestigious institutions, in addition to his undergraduate education. One of his doctorates is in pharmacology, and for a number of years he chaired the Department of Pharmacology at the School of Medicine, Loma Linda University. He has done primary research on the various effects of drugs in experimental animal models and has published many papers in peer-reviewed professional journals. Respected in the scientific community, he understands the scientific method. Furthermore, he knows both the value and limitations of modern drugs and the benefits and risks of medical herbs.

Surprisingly, he also has a grasp of preventative medicine, having long advocated that prevention is better than cure, and that living healthfully is the best way to have a long and disease-free life. For a number of years he served as the dean of the School of Public Health of Loma Linda University. The book you hold in your hands will give you both information and inspiration.

Elvin Adams, M.D.

INTRODUCTION
UNCERTAINTIES OF DRUG USE

Most people who respect the writings of Ellen White and who take seriously her counsels regarding medications hesitate at using drugs. When ill they may seek a physician's advice. But when the doctor prescribes drugs they feel guilty at the thought of taking medication, yet troubled if they don't. Others just try to put the issue aside, but still feel an inner concern. Still others console themselves that the counsel she gave against drugs in her day does not apply to those used in our day. And then a number turn to alternative medicine, botanic medicine, or vegetable drugs.

The Counsels on Drugs—Outdated?

Here we may pause to consider the way God presented the Bible. Its books were written in the setting of the time in which the human authors lived, reflecting the culture and lifestyle of those who wrote and of those to whom they directed their message. We read of slings, of shepherd's staffs, of walled cities, of potters making pots, of oil lamps and candles, of fishing boats, and of merchants in the marketplace. The parable of the sower and that of the 10 virgins are classic examples of writings reflecting a specific time and culture.

Because the message is framed in the milieu of the time does not make it any less important to the reader today. To the contrary, it gives the message greater force, for the illustrations used drive home the counsels. We can better understand the messages given by Ellen White and grasp their meaning more clearly when we can visualize the context and examples she employed. Recognizing the times in which she wrote in no way lessens the immediacy of the lesson for us.

It is for this reason that the author has attempted to provide at least a glimpse of the world in which Ellen White gave her ministry regarding the sick and the suffering. When illness struck during her lifetime, what did the patient have available in order to obtain relief? How well were physicians trained and how did they practice the healing art? What instruments did they have to aid them in making the diagnosis? And what medicines existed and how did they prescribe the various drugs?

Definition of Terms

Another problem has been that the author, along with many others with whom he has discussed the subject of this book, have defined the terms Ellen White used the way each thought best. Most have regarded drugs as any medicinal agent prescribed by a physician. "Simple remedies" were just uncomplicated and innocuous means of treating disease. I wonder how many readers have ever gone to a dictionary to see how it defines "simple"? When I did, I got a rude awakening (see chapter 3). I decided that I had better find out the real meaning of each word that I was interpreting. But even more important, have any of you carefully checked how Ellen White herself defined her terms?

The Origin of This Book

I first became interested in the subject of what Ellen White had to say about drugs and other remedies when I took a class in my freshman year of medical school (1937). As an assignment the teacher, Dr. E. H. Risley, required us to read two books, *The Ministry of Healing* and *Medical Ministry*. I bought and went through both books twice. To say the least, they intrigued me.

At the time I accepted Ellen White not as an inspired writer but only as a religious writer. Later as I checked statements she made about varying aspects of health with the scientific literature, I became convinced that without divine assistance she could not have written what she did or when she did. At the time of her writing such information simply was not readily available.

I would like to make it clear that throughout this work, whenever I state that "Ellen White said" something I am meaning that she was attempting to state that which she believed God had revealed to her.

Through the years I have struggled with what her message on therapeutics was really about. Back in 1945 I attempted to resolve the problem by placing her statements on drugs in chronological order, but that did little to help. Finally I decided that should God spare my life, I would thoroughly investigate the matter after I retired. And this I have done. Because others have called upon me to do many things since retirement, it delayed the research for several years. Finally, after diligent investigation and the enlightenment of the Holy Spirit, I place before the reader the insights I have gained.

Thank You

Many thanks to the readers, Neal C. Wilson, Alvin Adams, Merlin Burt, Ordell Calkins, Ian Fraser, Keith Hanson, and Jay Sloop, for their time and effort in appraising the manuscript and for their many helpful suggestions. I am indebted to the Ellen White Estate for providing me a computer printout of all Ellen White's statements on drugs, natural remedies, simple remedies, and herbs. This was before the CD-ROMs of her writing became available. The subsequent release of the disks have added greatly to the store of information. I wish to thank Merlin D. Burt, chair of the archives and special collections, Del E. Webb Memorial Library and Ellen White Publications, Loma Linda University, and Janice White and other members of his staff for their tireless efforts in tracking down the original source of every statement. To Fred, my son, and daughter, Jeanne Ekvall, deep gratitude for their constant willingness to solve computer glitches and manuscript holdups as it progressed from start to finish. And to my good wife, Margaret, for her quiet patience. And finally, the author deeply appreciates the careful and thorough work of Gerald Wheeler, together with his associates, in editing the manuscript and bringing it into shape.

The volume of material available for each topic covered in the book is immense, such as medical education or medical practice in Ellen White's time. The focus of this work does not allow us to go into depth on any of these topics. The same is true of, for example, the mechanism of how drugs work or the placebo effect. I have had to address such areas only sketchily. However, I have provided the reader sufficient material to lead to an informed decision.

The conclusions of the study did not turn out the way I had anticipated, because I had not at first defined the terms *simple remedies* or *drugs* the way Ellen White had. I had to discard my prior interpretations to fit the facts. It was only with these understandings, and when I viewed the counsels as a whole, that God's directives as to therapeutic reform and the lifestyle He desired for His people finally came into focus.

The Book's Purpose

It is my prayer that God will give each reader "a wise and an understanding heart" (1 Kings 3:12) and provide a grasp of the subject that he or she may not have previously had.

> "I stand by the side of a river
> As it enters the restless sea.
> And men of all sorts from many ports
> Come in to be healed by me.
> And some have more sin than sickness,
> And some have more grief than pain.
> Lord, help me to make whole, both body and soul,
> Before they go out again."
>
> —*Anonymous*
> (printed in *Adventist Review*, December 1998, p. 30)

CHAPTER ONE

A Physician Explains . . .

MEDICAL EDUCATION IN ELLEN WHITE'S DAY

SECTION I

The Training of Regular Physicians

Ellen White spoke and wrote extensively in the areas of both therapeutics and health reform. To appreciate better the counsels God gave through her in these fields, we need to understand the type and quality of the medical education physicians of her day received, as well as the way the medical community practiced medicine during her lifetime. In this chapter we shall consider medical education during the nineteenth century.

Preceptorships

For some two centuries during the Colonial period and the early years of independence, medical students in the United States obtained their medical education by apprenticing themselves to a physician, who was called a preceptor. The period of the preceptorship usually lasted three years.[1] The apprentice frequently boarded with the physician, who provided the necessary books and equipment.

The student first became acquainted with the medical literature (being wholly dependent on the preceptor's library), did odd jobs around the home and office, collected medicinal roots and herbs, compounded prescriptions (few pharmacists yet existed), and even groomed and saddled the doctor's horse! As the student's knowledge increased, he (medicine was a male profession) began "riding with the doctor," making house calls, and assisting with bloodletting and surgeries. It was the extent of his medical education.[2]

Depending on the ability and faithfulness of both the preceptor and student, the training might be shoddy or excellent. Since the medical community had no way to evaluate either, the certificate obtained at the end of the apprenticeship period meant little.[3]

During the early years of the nineteenth century the rigid line we draw today between the trained and licensed physician and any other less qualified "practitioners" of the healing arts simply did not exist. Competing with the apprentice-trained physicians were midwives, bone-setters, apothecaries, and other itinerant "specialists" claiming to treat eye ailments and "secret diseases." And mothers who took care of all the minor ailments of their children, some gaining repute in the community, supplemented the various quasimedical practitioners. Most homes had books, family medical guides, to which members referred when illness struck.[4]

Medical Schools Gradually Develop

As the demand for apprenticeships increased and notable physicians obtained large numbers of apprentices, classroom teaching became necessary. A group of physicians, especially in urban areas, would set up their own school, frequently associated with a local liberal arts college. The college awarded the degrees while the members of the medical society offered the courses. The establishment of the medical schools of Pennsylvania, Columbia, and Harvard universities followed such a pattern.

When no local college existed, some physicians might seek a charter from the state to form a corporation, operate a medical school, and grant degrees. As the medical schools proliferated, they competed with the apprenticeship system. With the growth of scientific knowledge in anatomy, physiology, chemistry, and microbiology, the influence and attractiveness of the medical school increased, especially those that could provide essential laboratory teaching.

The Curricula and Length of Study

One feature of the school programs involved the matter of curricula, determined in part by the length of the term. The first lectures at Harvard, given by Dr. John Warren and his associates, lasted only a few weeks. By 1809 the term of instruction had lengthened to eight weeks, and a year later to approximately three months. As the century progressed practically all the schools adopted a single term of three to four months. The American Medical Association began after 1847 to urge medical schools to lengthen their term of instruction to six months.[5]

The Need for Controls and Standards

Medical education was for the most part a matter of private enterprise. Several physicians living in the same locality united to provide medical instruction. At the end of the course of study they awarded testimonials of proficiency. No one evaluated the qualifications of those who taught or how much the students had actually learned. Financial concerns motivated the organizers of most schools, and the scandalous practices of many faculties created great notoriety. The Philadelphia *Record*, on February 28, 1880, published a report of their investigation of "a doctor factory making full-fledged physicians for seventy-five dollars."[6] Diploma mills were all too common.

Not all schools, however, offered weak courses. Among those enjoying a high reputation were the New York College of Physicians and Surgeons; the Bellevue Hospital College, New York; the Massachusetts Medical College, Boston; and the Rush Medical College, Chicago. By 1885, 95 percent of medical schools had a two-year course of training. Unfortunately, the courses in the second year often repeated those given earlier, and the schools encouraged the students to pick up any information they had missed on the first exposure![7]

Many schools permitted medical students to take a one-year preceptorship in lieu of formal training at a college. President Charles W. Eliot, of Harvard, in his report for the year 1871-1872, has left us this desolating picture: "It is fearful to think of the ignorance and incompetence of most American doctors who have graduated at American schools. They poison, maim, and do men to death in various ways, and are unable to save life or preserve health."[8]

Standards Finally Established

Fortunately times were changing. The basic sciences were developing to undergird clinical training. By 1899, of 155 medical schools (one failed to report) 91 percent had four-year programs, 7 percent had three-year programs, while one had a two- and another a one-year term.[9]

But even as recently as 1910, Abraham Flexner of the Carnegie Foundation for the Advancement of Teaching, in his famous report on the evaluation of medical education in the United States and Canada, describes, for example, the deplorable conditions present in the Georgia College of Eclectic Medicine and Surgery.

"Laboratory facilities: The school occupies a building which, in respect to filthy conditions, has few equals, but no superiors, among medical schools. Its anatomy room, containing a single cadaver, is indescribably foul; its chemical 'laboratory' is composed of old tables and a few bottles, without water, drain, lockers, or reagents; the pathological and histological 'laboratory' contains a few dirty slides and three ordinary microscopes. . . . Nothing more disgraceful calling itself a medical school can be found anywhere."[10]

Some of the pioneer physicians in the Seventh-day Adventist Church, who received their training during the final quarter of the nineteenth century, received criticism from certain writers because of the "short" period of training they underwent before becoming qualified in medicine. An understanding of what actually constituted formal medical training during the formative years of our church provides a perspective that, it is hoped, allows for a true evaluation of our early medical people. We will discuss this further in the next chapter.

SECTION II

Ellen White and Medical Education

As an educator, Ellen White endorsed and encouraged the training of ministers, Bible instructors, teachers, nurses, physicians, and anyone taking up any field of service. Of the unique counsels and instructions she gave regarding the education of nurses and physicians (and this is what we are dealing with in the context of drugs), five points stand out. The first emphasized high standards and quality training. The second required instruction in the Scriptures, an understanding of Bible truths. The third encouraged the highest quality of sick care. The fourth directed medical practice to focus on lifestyle change and preventive medicine. And the fifth emphasized health promotion. The latter concept was foreign to the medical education at the time, and is still in advance of much of the training given medical and nursing students today.

High Standards and Quality Training

Ellen White repeatedly encouraged nurses and physicians to obtain "superior skill, fitted to stand upon the highest eminence" ([1913] CT 470). Notice the following: "Every physician, every nurse, every helper, who has anything to do with God's service, must aim at perfection." She goes on to say that there must be no "superficial knowledge" but that the training "must be painstaking and thorough" *(ibid.)*.

"Those in training to be nurses and physicians should daily be given instruction that will develop the highest motives for advancement" *(ibid. 520)*.

Bible Truths in Medical Curricula

No other curriculum in nursing or medicine required Bible study as part of its course work. Yet Ellen White believed that instruction in sacred truth should complement scientific training: "Besides the special science required that [men and women] may be intelligent physicians, [they] need a daily training in the school of Christ, that they may learn to work as Jesus worked, in purity, in unselfishness, in holiness before God" (letter 41, 1890, quoted in 1MR 212).

"I am intensely interested in the education of medical students as missionaries. . . . How essential that the living missionary should understand the diseases which afflict the human body, to combine the physician, educated to care for diseased bodies, with the faithful, conscientious shepherd of the flock, to give sacredness and double efficiency to the service!" (*The Gospel of Health,* June 1, 1897).

"The cause of God today would have been far in advance of what it is, had we in former years been more active in the training of nurses who, in addition to their requirement of more than ordinary skill in the care of the sick, had also learned to labor as evangelists in soul-winning service" ([1913] CT 471).

Women and Men to Receive Equal Training

"Women as well as men are to receive a thorough medical training. . . . It is just as essential that women receive such training, and obtain their diplomas certifying their right to act as physicians" (letter 22, 1911, quoted in MM 61).

Ellen White Foresaw Nurse-Practitioners

"'A special work is to be done there in qualifying young men and young women to be efficient medical missionary workers. They are to be taught how to treat the sick without the use of drugs.' . . . In harmony with this instruction, the school was established with three years' medical evangelistic course, supplemented by a strong three years' nurses course, designed to qualify workers with all the ability of physicians, in harmony with the testimonies given" (letter B-90, 1908, LLM 412).

Change Unhealthful Habits and Prevent Disease

Her concept of training nurses and physicians to focus on the unhealthful habits of the sick, and encouraging them to adopt more healthful ones, was foreign to the thinking of the rank and file nurse or physician of her day. Although a few believed that "nature should be given a chance" to heal a person and urged patients to exercise, rest, and eat nutritiously, *none believed that the ultimate focus should be lifestyle change, and that medicinal therapy was but the initial step toward a healthful way of life.*

"The *first* labors of a physician should be to educate the sick and suffering in the very course they should pursue to prevent disease" (manuscript 22, 1887, quoted in MM 221; italics supplied).

"He [the physician] will, if a reformer, talk plainly in regard to the false appetites and ruinous self-indulgence, in dressing, in eating and drinking, in overtaxing to do a large amount of work in a given time, which has a ruinous influence upon the temper, the physical and mental powers. . . . Right and correct habits, intelligently and perseveringly practiced, will be removing the cause for disease, and the strong drugs need not be resorted to" *(ibid. 222)*.

A Superb Promise

"The light that God has given in medical missionary lines will not cause His people to be regarded as inferior in scientific medical knowledge, but will fit them to stand upon the highest eminence. God would have them stand as a wise and understanding people because of His presence with them. In the strength of Him who is the Source of all wisdom, all grace, defects and ignorance may be overcome" ([1913] CT 476).

Success Promised

Such a system of medical training vastly differed from what was available in contemporary medical schools, although some of the better medical schools taught a technical medicine more advanced than the denomination's schools could offer. However, because of the avoidance of the powerful drugs commonly in use, the simple physiological measures used, the elimination of unhealthful habits of eating and living, and the blending of the emotional and spiritual needs of the sick, together with prayer in the sickroom, Adventist health centers obtained better results than the best conventional methods then in use. Battle Creek Sanitarium and its fellow institutions rose to preeminence and earned a favorable reputation around the world.

Summary

Beginning in the midnineteenth century and continuing for the next 60 years, rapid and significant changes occurred in medical education. Advancing knowledge in human physiology, microbiology (with the discovery of germs), and other basic sciences transformed the content of what medical schools taught their students. It shook the very foundations of medical education. Beyond this, clinical training, shifting from a dubious preceptorship to practical experience under the instruction of qualified clinicians in a hospital setting, radically altered the very nature of how the sick were treated.

A new generation of young physicians arrived on the scene who no longer held to the traditions of the past. Medical and health reformers (to be discussed later) introduced new concepts regarding the cause and treatment of disease. Ellen White was one of those reformers, who attacked not only the system of current medical practice, but also the way physicians then received their education. She encouraged the thorough training of physicians and nurses, not just to care for the sick but to help their patients change their unhealthful habits and prevent further suffering. It was a new and revolutionary concept.

She recommended that the spiritual training they received during their education should aid physicians and nurses to pray with the sick and suffering, pointing them to their Healer and Saviour. Further, she urged that God be brought into the sickroom and stated that with His blessing Adventist medical personnel would accomplish great things. The reputation that Battle Creek Sanitarium gained quickly testified to the success that followed obedience to God's counsel.

References
[1] F. W. Norwood, *Medical Education in the United States Before the Civil War* (New York: Arno Press and the New York *Times,* 1971), p. 380.

[2] William G. Rothstein, *American Physicians in the Nineteenth Century: From Sects to Science* (Baltimore: Johns Hopkins University Press, 1972), pp. 85-87; Francis R. Packard, *History of Medicine in the United States* (New York: Hafner Pub. Co., 1963), vol. 1, p. 286.

[3] Alfred Stille, *Medical Education in the United States: An Address* (Philadelphia: Isaac Ashmead, 1846), pp. 18, 19.

[4] George Rosen, *The Structure of American Medical Practice, 1875-1941* (Philadelphia: University of Pennsylvania Press, 1983), pp. 3, 4; Richard H. Shryock, *Medicine in America: Historical Essays* (Baltimore: Johns Hopkins Press, 1966), pp. 62, 63.

[5] Norwood, p. 402.

[6] Theodor Puschmann, *A History of Medical Education* (New York: Hartner Pub. Co., Inc., 1966, facsimile of 1891 edition), p. 534.

[7] Rothstein, p. 288.

[8] Puschmann, p. 534.

[9] Rothstein, p. 288.

[10] Abraham Flexner, *Medical Education in the United States and Canada: A Report to the Carnegie Foundation for the Advancement of Teaching* (1910), Bulletin No. 4, pp. 204, 205.

CHAPTER TWO

A Physician Explains . . .

THE PRACTICE OF MEDICINE IN ELLEN WHITE'S DAY

This chapter offers a brief glimpse as to how physicians practiced medicine during Ellen White's lifetime, especially the early years of her prophetic ministry. Hopefully it will provide a better understanding of the counsels she gave about drug therapy during this period. The author must emphasize that the face of medicine was changing at an accelerating pace throughout the second half of the nineteenth century.

SECTION I

Traditional Medicine

"Therapy in the seventeenth century was mainly a continuation of the past in terms of bleeding, purging, dietary restriction, exercise, and the use of nonspecific plant, mineral, and animal drugs. One new medication, however, was a striking departure in the effectiveness and in general influence on the principles of therapy: quinine—as a treatment for malaria."[1]

Throughout the eighteenth and most of the nineteenth centuries the only real means of diagnosing disease were the patient's obvious symptoms. Medicine, as a result, classified diseases according to symptoms. For example, physicians categorized fevers as "remittent, intermittent, and continuing," depending on how they came and went. They arranged pain according to type: dull, sharp, throbbing, burning, lancinating, gnawing, and vicelike. Those diseases with striking but superficial symptoms physicians would identify by size and color: great pox (syphilis), small pox, yellow fever, scarlet fever, etc.[2] In addition, they considered combinations of symptoms as separate illnesses, producing, as a consequence, long lists of "confusing diseases," that were really just so many meaningless names.[3]

During the early period of the eighteenth century the popular belief held that an imbalance in the "humors," a term referring to the internal body fluids, led to sickness and disease. By midcentury theories that disease resulted from abnormal states of tension in the nervous and vascular systems gradually replaced the humor concept. At times the patient might experience "excitability," or at other periods states of "debility." Imbalance of one over the other resulted in disease.[4]

Benjamin Rush

Benjamin Rush (1745-1813) would have a powerful impact on this concept of illness. One of America's most famous physicians of his day, he was both a forceful speaker and a prolific writer. He believed that debility was a cause of illness and not a disease in itself and that the disease state was always a result of "morbid excitement" or excessive tension in the nervous and vascular systems. Fever, for example, was a spasm of "the extreme arteries" or capillaries.[5]

Eventually he carried the medical doctrine to excess. "Not only fevers but all types of illness were ascribed to capillary tension. Therefore, he informed his students, there was really *'only one disease in the world.'* "[6] This conclusion would naturally lead to another: there was *only one treatment!* And what better way of relieving vascular tension than by bleeding and purging. This too he carried to the extreme.

The vigor with which he applied his conviction earned him the title "Master Bleeder," and he would continue the process, when necessary, till he had drained the patient of four fifths of all the blood in the body. We could summarize Rush's formula for treatment as purges, vomits, bleeding, blisters, sweats, and opium, to which one could add generous doses of calomel (mercury) and antimony. As bleeding proceeded, along with one or more other procedures, "excessive action" decreased and, given time, sooner or later the patient relaxed! His theory was irrefutable.[7]

Some physicians recognized the inherent healing power of nature, but Rush would have none of it. He believed that the physician must banish nature from the sickroom. William Cobbett denounced Rush's practice of extreme bleeding and purging, as "one of those great discoveries which are made from time to time for the depopulation of the earth."[8]

When the Physician Arrived—Common Procedures

Physicians generally prescribed drugs that caused drastic and prolonged effects. When one agent failed to give prompt action, they employed another, or combinations of several. Here are some of the procedures that they used almost routinely.[9]

Bloodletting—The doctor removed blood by lancing or cutting into an artery. Some, such as Rush, withdrew up to four fifths of the body's total blood supply. Cupping was commonly used. Physicians applied leeches to infants and children whose arteries were too small to lance or cut into. If they wanted to withdraw more blood, they employed larger numbers of leeches.[10]

Vomiting—Early American medicine turned to emetics (zinc sulphate, mustard, apomorphine, ipecac, tartar emetic) to trigger vomiting.

Purging—Doctors resorted to chemical agents (such as mercury, antimony, magnesium sulfate [Epsom salts]) or herbs (podophyllum, colocynth, jalap, croton oil) to empty the bowels. Called drastics, such harsh agents often scoured the intestinal tract so that the stools consisted of a bloody flux.

Expectorating—Chemicals and herbals (ammonium chloride, squill, senega, licorice) increased the flow of saliva and the secretions of the respiratory system, specifically the trachea and bronchi.

Sweating—Diaphoretics (sweet spirits of niter, camphor, jaborandi) caused profuse sweating.

Urinating—Diuretics (squill, scoparius) increased the flow of urine.

If physicians considered the previous treatments insufficient, then they turned to **blistering** the poor patient. They applied mustard plasters, cantharides, and other irritants to the skin of the chest, back, arms, thighs, and even the back of the neck, producing massive blisters filled with fluid.

Frequently a physician would use the procedures of bleeding, vomiting, purging, expectorating, sweating, urinating, and blistering all at the same time. As a result of the concerted effort to deplete the body of its fluids, or of ridding the vessels and nervous system of their "excessive action," a maddening thirst would develop in the sufferer. The doctor then routinely restricted the intake of water altogether, and if given any, the patient could take it only in sips, and then often with salt, so as, supposedly, not to distend or excite the stomach.[11]

SECTION II

Unbelievable Procedures

The author does not wish to weary the reader. However, without having a clear picture of what the reformers of the times, including Ellen White, combated, we naturally think in terms of how physicians practice medicine today. Let us briefly fill out the sketchy outline presented above.

Bloodletting

"I was acquainted with a neighboring physician who proposed to cure and did cure common intermittent [malaria] by bloodletting alone; he bled the patient till he was too weak to shake, and the disease and the patient went off together. I mention [this] to show the recklessness of doctors in the use of the lancet, and of patients in submitting to it. . . .

"It was fortunate in that day that we had a hardy, well developed race of men and women, possessing sufficient tenacity of life to not only resist the disease, but the remedies used to combat it."[12]

"The most extraordinary fact was not that bloodletting was used so widely, but that blood was drawn in such large quantities and repeated over such a length of time. One physician wrote in 1851 that he administered the following treatment to a woman who had just been delivered of a child and was suffering from puerperal convulsions (childbed fever):

" 'I opened a large orifice in each arm and cut both temporal arteries and had blood flowing freely from all at the same time, determined to bleed her until the convulsions ceased, or as long as the blood would flow. How much she bled, I have no means of judging, for I designedly prevented any attempt to catch the blood and the convulsions were so violent and so frequent it could not have been caught if attempted. I suffered her to bleed until the pulse could not be felt at the wrist, and beat but feebly in the carotid arteries [located above and in front of the ears] by which time the convulsions ceased. . . . The woman recovered rapidly without subsequent inconvenience. . . . My practice has been to bleed as long as I thought the bleeding itself would not endanger life. I prefer to cut the temporal arteries in bad cases.' "[13]

Such extreme efforts frequently had tragic consequences. Salmon P. Chase, Abraham Lincoln's secretary of the treasury and later chief justice of the United States, described the death of his first wife, two weeks after childbirth, in Cincinnati about 1837. The family believed that she had puerperal fever, and sent for the family physician, a Dr. Colby. He in turn requested a consultation with Dr. Daniel Drake. Chase wrote in his diary:

"Before he arrived Dr. Colby had made preparations for bleeding her, thinking prompt bloodletting necessary, and that a high peritoneal inflammation existed. Dr. Drake concurred, and they proceeded to bleed. When six or eight ounces were abstracted, Dr. Colby, thinking she had been bled as much as her constitution would bear, and becoming satisfied from the effect of the bleeding that the high state of inflammation supposed did not really exist, arrested the flow of blood. Dr. Drake was much dissatisfied, and insisted on more copious bleeding. The bandage was accordingly removed, and more blood taken. It was then replaced. Dr. Drake still remained unsatisfied, urging that it was necessary to bleed to fainting. [The difference of opinion was presented to the family, and Dr. Richards was brought in. Drs. Richards and Drake] both soon agreed as to the necessity of bleeding, and she was again bled. . . . Forty grains of calomel were then administered. Thirty ounces of blood had been taken. Still Drs. Drake and Richards were not satisfied—they thought further bleeding was necessary, yet postponed it till morning. . . .

" '[The next morning.] Such was her condition on the morning of this unhappy day, there was a fair prospect of her recovery. All the symptoms boded well. But Drs. Drake and Richards were of the opinion that she had not been bled sufficiently, and that the disease had not been subdued. They accordingly recommended further bleeding; Dr. Colby opposed it, saying that all her symptoms were improved, and they ought to watch the result. The other physicians insisted, however. [A fourth physician, Dr. Eberle, was sent for.] He concurred with the majority, and further bleeding was consequently resolved upon. It was anticipated that the effect would be to reduce the frequency of the pulse, and augment its volume! Kitty was told that the doctors thought of bleeding her again, and was asked if she was willing. She said, "Yes, anything." She was then raised up in bed, and twenty ounces of blood were taken from her. *The effect on the pulse was the exact contrary of what was anticipated.* It became more frequent and more feeble, but in other respects she seemed somewhat easier. The physicians seemed to entertain some hopes of her recovery, and agreed upon a course of treatment to be adopted. The [patient's] father came into [her] room exclaiming, "Thank God, my child, the doctors say there is hope." She said nothing. All hope had vanished. . . . Dr. Drake felt her pulse, and said she was dead.' "[14]

Blisters

Early nineteenth-century physicians commonly used blistering to treat fevers, as we see in the following contemporary accounts.

"In intermittents [fever], they [blisters] are sometimes highly useful as a preventive of the paroxysm. . . . Constantly kept on the extremities, the irritation which they induce will, after a time, so interrupt the trains of morbid association, constituting this form of fever, as frequently to put an end to the worst cases of it. . . . Nor are they [blisters] less demanded, in those cases of the disease attended by visceral congestion, or induration of a painful and inflammatory nature. They should here be applied immediately over the affected part. . . . A succession of blisters ought never to be neglected. . . . I have also found that it is . . . one of the most decisive means of arousing the recuperative energies, where reaction is refused in the cold stage of the pernicious forms of the disease.

"As to typhus fever, a course somewhat different should be pursued. . . . There is, in every stage of the disease, evidence of undue determination to this organ [the brain], the removal of which is most effectually accomplished, after general measures—by cold applications to the part—topical depletion by leeches or cups, and, by a blister in the first place, to the nape of the neck, and next, should it be required, over the whole cranium."[15]

"Most writers agree as to the utility of blistering in it [dysentery], differing, however, in relation to the part where the application is to be made. Influenced by the apprehension of excessive pain when made to the abdomen, the extremities are often preferred. This is an instance of mischievous lenity proceeding, I am persuaded, from an erroneous impression. Delayed, which it ought always to be, till the force of inflammatory action is abated, a blister is then productive of comparatively little distress while drawing, and, sometimes, by the ease and comfort which it affords, even composes to sleep. . . .

"Of the utility of blisters in rheumatism, no one doubts."[16]

The physician applied the blisters to the thighs and legs, usually avoiding the abdomen because many felt they were too painful there. However, Dr. Chapman believed (see above) such a course to be "an instance of mischievous lenity." Lenity means lenient, or the desire to relieve pain and distress. In dealing with typhus Dr. Chapman applied blisters, one to the back of the neck and another over the entire scalp. Medical doctors commonly employed croton oil and mustard. At the same time they bled their patients and gave them purgatives to make the bowels move. It is, indeed, hard to believe that people would submit to such things.

The Business of Drugging

During the period of apprenticeships, one of the responsibilities of the apprentice was to learn from his mentor how to identify medicinal herbs. Rural areas, especially, had no other source of "medicines." Physicians had to be their own apothecaries. They and their assistants harvested, dried, made into pills, or extracted the herbal medicine. But this changed over time. It could not be done in the larger cities, and besides, the physicians were too busy to go out into the country to collect herbs.

Since such herbs offered a ready source of income, men and women gradually learned to collect those of medicinal value. The herbalists eventually became apothecaries, and in due time local governing bodies began to license them. They often counseled the sick and in many instances did the work of a physician. As in Europe so in this country a certain rivalry arose between the medical practitioner and the apothecary. When apothecaries became the source of the medicines that the doctors prescribed, physicians would, on occasion, write prescriptions but would omit the instructions, giving them only to the patient. The apothecaries retaliated by making referrals only to physicians who prescribed large numbers of drugs![17] So those physicians who attempted therapeutic reforms soon had problems.

Emetics and Purgatives—To Cleanse the Stomach and Bowels

Again contemporary accounts demonstrate the drastic measures nineteenth-century medicine employed.

"One country physician recalled: 'If vomited, they did not come up in gentle puffs and gusts, but the action was cyclonic. If, perchance, the stomach was passed the expulsion would be by the rectum and anus, and this would be equal to a regular oil-well gusher.'"[18]

Medical historian Rothstein comments that "unfortunately, calomel [mercurous chloride] had side effects that were detrimental to health. One physician distinguished three gradations of the action of the drug. In the first stage, purging and salivation occurred. In the second stage, the gums, tongue, and salivary glands became sore, inflamed, and painful. Soon, according to another writer, if the dosing were continued:

" 'The mouth feels unusually hot, and is sometimes sensible of a coppery or metallic taste; the gums are swollen, red, and tender; ulcers make their appearance and spread in all directions; the saliva is thick and stringy, and has that peculiar, offensive odor characteristic of mercurial disease; the tongue is swollen and stiff, and there is some fever, with derangement of the secretions. The disease progressing, it destroys every part that it touches, until the lips, the cheeks, and even the bones have been eaten away before death comes to the sufferer's relief.'

"The most common and noticeable effect of calomel appears to have been on the teeth and mouth:

" 'The teeth, those valuable instruments of our most substantial enjoyments, become loose and rot, perhaps fall out; or worse still, the upper and lower jaw-bones exfoliate and rot out sometimes, as I have witnessed in the form of horse shoes; parts of the tongue and palate are frequently lost, and the poor object lingers out a doleful existence during life. . . . This happens when mercury per-forms *a cure!* ' " [19]

"The effect of these purgatives on the patient's system was de-bilitating and dehydrating in the extreme. One physician con-demned his colleagues' callousness in their frequent resort to purgatives and urged them to take some of their own medicine so as to cause five or six evacuations a day for a week. He said, *'It will take all your strength, your flesh, your blood, your appetite, your func-tions of all kinds, just as certainly as a bloodletting, and you will be able to realize the influence of similar catharsis on the sick.'* " [20]

Sympathy Based on Ignorance!

"One physician reminisced that in the early decades of the cen-tury, 'when a practitioner was puzzled about the administration of any medicine in a disease, it was deemed perfectly proper for him to prescribe a dose of calomel; which he did conscientiously, with well satisfied assurance, that if he did not give the exact medicine adapted to the case, he could not be far wrong!' Many physicians believed that omission of calomel in desperate cases was tantamount to abandoning the patient without a final saving effort."[21]

George Washington—His Final Illness and Death

The death of George Washington offers one of the most dramatic examples of the dangers of early American medical practice. On Friday, December 13, 1799, Washington was exposed to a cold rain. Sometime during the night he had a bout of violent ague (a fever marked by paroxysms of chills alternating with fever and sweating) with pain in his upper throat, some difficulty in swallowing, and a slight cough. A fever and labored breathing followed the ague.

Washington, who believed in the benefits of bleeding, sent for a neighborhood bleeder, who removed some 13 ounces (370 milliliters) of blood. About 11:00 Saturday morning his own physician arrived. He decided to send for two consultants, who arrived late in the afternoon. While waiting for their arrival, he bled Washington twice. The accounts do not specify the amount of blood removed, but do record "two copious bleedings." He also gave the former president two doses of calomel (a cathartic), applied a blister to the front of his neck, and washed out his lower bowel with an enema. All his efforts produced no benefit. Washington's breathing had become labored.

After the two consultants arrived, the three physicians, after discussing the case among themselves, decided to try another bleeding. This time they drained 32 ounces (900 milliliters) of blood, with no apparent benefit. In addition, they repeatedly gave their patient vapors of vinegar and water to breathe, several doses of tartar emetic to keep him vomiting, and a large dose of calomel to keep his bowels active. He had a large bowel movement, but his general condition worsened. Next they applied blisters to his legs and a bran poultice to his throat. Washington's breathing became more difficult until he could speak only in whispers, and about 11:00 Saturday night he died.[22]

As best as we can gather, Washington's exposure to a cold rain on Friday brought on a sore throat or pharyngitis and laryngitis, an inflammation of his voice box. Washington himself, a believer in bleeding, ordered the first blood to be taken.

Part of his treatment consisted of four bleedings. His first involved about 13 ounces (370 milliliters). We can only estimate the amounts of blood drawn for his second and third procedures, although the historical records describe them as "two copious bleedings." Since his final bleeding was 32 ounces, let's estimate that his third and fourth bleedings were 24 ounces (675 milliliters) each. The total blood withdrawn, conservatively comes to 2,600 milliliters, more than two and one-half liters. It has been estimated that Washington, for his build and age, would probably have had seven liters of blood. The therapy drained Washington of roughly 40 percent of his blood. If the "copious bleedings" were in amounts the same as his final bleeding, the doctors could easily have withdrawn half of his blood.[23]

They administered two moderate and one large dose of calomel. Calomel is a rather harsh cathartic. Also he received an enema. Repeated doses of tartar emetic induced vomiting. In addition, they blistered him on his front upper neck as well as his lower "extremities." Usually the procedure involved large blisters on the thighs and calves. To add to the misery, they intermittently asked him to breathe "vapors of vinegar."

Can you picture what occurred? A strong man developed a severe laryngitis. His doctors withdrew half of his blood, scoured his bowels with doses of cathartics, gave him an enema, and made him vomit repeatedly while breathing vinegar vapors. The blisters on his neck, thigh, and legs must have been like torture. And all this going on at the same time! It was enough to kill a man— and it did.

While some physicians criticized the treatment given Washington, I believe that Paul Leicester Ford sums up the whole incident: "There can be scarcely a doubt that the treatment of his last illness by the doctors was little short of murder."[24]

A physician stated in 1849 that for many of his fellow medical professionals "the lancet, mercury, antimony or opium, are the great guns that they always fire on all occasions. . . . Whoever sends for a physician of this sort expects to be bled, blistered or vomited, or submitted to some other painful or nauseous medication."[25]

A Point to Ponder

You are a physician practicing medicine in 1865. Someone knocks at your door at midnight. A man with a concerned expression begs you to come and attend his wife, whom, he believes, is dying. Entering his house, you look into the ashen face of an extremely sick woman. The questions you ask her husband yield nothing. What will you do?

Checking her pulse, you find it weak and irregular. Next, placing your ear on her chest, you attempt to listen to the heart sounds and the rattles in her lungs. But regardless of what you hear there is nothing you have that can do any good.

Because you have no thermometer to check her temperature, you place your hand on her brow. It feels hot and dry. But you have no sphygmomanometer to check her blood pressure or stethoscope to listen to the sounds of her lungs, her heart, or her abdomen with any clarity. Worst of all, you have no ambulance or hospital to take her to. If a hospital did exist, it would have no clinical laboratory to run tests on urine, blood, or spinal fluid; no X-ray unit to check her lungs or do a CAT scan; no electrocardiogram to monitor her heartbeats; no intravenous fluids, no transfusions, no antibiotics—nothing!

But wait! You have in your doctor bag a lancet and some killer drugs. Would you watch her die, or would you do something? And if you did do something, what would it be?

Now consider a different scenario. Instead of attacking your patient with bleeding, purging, and vomiting, you allow nature a chance by giving her water to drink, placing a cool cloth to her brow, letting fresh air into the sickroom, and perhaps providing a nourishing broth. A prayer offered to the Great Physician would not be out of place. If the patient is to die, may she die in peace and comfort. A few courageous physicians did just what we have suggested. But we should also remember that many patients, together with their relatives, demanded that "something" be done. They believed in drastic measures. And despite such extreme treatment, some managed to survive—even if only half alive!

The Coming Medical Revolution

The thermometer did not become an integral part of medicine until the latter part of the nineteenth century. Aitkin (1852) made the mercury column in the glass tube more narrow so that the fluid did not fall back. However, it was not until 1870 that Thomas Allbutt designed the clinical thermometer employed today.

The so-called double stethoscope did not come into use until the beginning of the twentieth century, though some physicians had tried a prototype consisting of a single wooden tube some 10 years earlier.

The sphygmomanometer developed during the same time period as the stethoscope. It enabled the physician to determine both the high and the lower level of blood pressure (systolic and diastolic).[26]

It was during Ellen White's lifetime that great men such as Semmelweis, Pasteur, and Lister, sometimes under daunting circumstances, introduced the concepts of asepsis (c. 1850), bacteria (1850), viruses (c. 1875), and built on the work of Jenner (1798) to provide a variety of vaccines for the growing number of identified infectious diseases.[27]

Reform and a Reformer

The preceding examples and quotes give but a glimpse of the murderous medicine practiced during the early part of Ellen White's life. To prevent the misery and death of the growing number of God's people, He showed her some of the hazards of taking powerful drugs, and she warned all who would listen. But best of all, she proposed ways of both preventing sickness and treating disease. She pointed out a better way that gave hope to the sick and brought relief to the suffering, as the following pages will reveal.

References

[1] Albert S. Lyons and R. Joseph Petrucelli II, *Medicine: An Illustrated History* (New York: Harry N. Abrams, Inc., 1978), p. 454. Quinine, obtained from cinchona bark, specifically attacked the parasites causing certain common forms of malaria.

[2] R. H. Shryock, *Medicine in America: Historical Essays,* pp. 4, 5.

[3] W. G. Rothstein, *American Physicians,* pp. 42, 43; Thomas Jefferson expressed himself on this point: "The adventurous physician . . . substitutes presumption for knowledge. From the scanty field of what is known, he launches into the boundless region of what is unknown. He establishes for his guide some fanciful theory of corpuscular attraction, of chemical agency, of mechanical powers, of stimuli, of irritability accumulated or exhausted, of depletion by the lancet and repletion by mercury, or some other ingenious dream, which lets him into all nature's secrets at short hand. On the principle which he thus assumes, he forms his table of nosology [classification or list of diseases], arrays his diseases into families, and extends his curative treatment, by analogy, to all the cases he has thus arbitrarily marshalled together. I have lived myself to see the disciples of [a number of theorists] succeed one another like the shifting figures of a magic lantern, and their fancies, like the dresses of the annual doll-babies from Paris, becoming, from their novelty, the vogue of the day, and yielding to the next novelty their ephemeral favor" (Rothstein, p. 42).

[4] R H. Shryock, *Medicine and Society in America,* pp. 66-69; Medicine in America, pp. 239, 240.

[5] Shryock, *Medicine in America,* p. 69.

[6] *Ibid.,* pp. 69, 70. (Italics supplied.)

[7] *Ibid.,* pp. 205-207.

[8] *Ibid.,* p. 207.

[9] George B. Wood, *Treatise on the Practice of Medicine,* third ed. (Philadelphia: Lippincott, Grambo, and Co., 1852), Vol. I, pp. 213-216.

[10] A report from Stanford University entitled "Stanford Surgical Helpers Are Out for Blood" describes a recent experience, and I quote: "Thirty years of skin cancer operations had gradually whittled away William Rambo's nose, so he was delighted when surgeon Richard Goode, M.D., promised to make him a new one. But the retired Stanford professor of electrical engineering owes his new look to more than Goode's skill at molding a replacement nose from a swatch of Rambo's scalp. Because even before the anesthetic had worn off, stagnant blood began to swamp the relocated tissue, coloring it a sickly blue. To relieve the blood buildup and salvage the transplant, Goode was obliged to call for a rarely used but powerful therapy, the best available to modern high-tech medicine. He prescribed a course of hungry leeches. That's right, leeches. After a century of exile, these slippery creatures have crept back to medical respectability, thanks to their unmatched ability to drain excess blood from injured tissue" (Mitch Leslie, *Stanford Medicine,* Spring 1999, p. 17). The clock comes full circle!

[11] Watson, *Lectures on the Principles & Practice of Physic,* American ed. (Blanchard and Lea, 1858), p. 1145.

[12] Rothstein, p. 46.

[13] *Ibid.,* p. 47.

[14] *Ibid.,* pp. 47, 48.

[15] Nathaniel Chapman, *Elements of Therapeutics and Materia Medica,* 6th ed. (Philadelphia: Casey and Lea, 1831), pp. 31, 32.

[16] *Ibid.,* p. 35.

[17] Lyons and Petrucelli, p. 447.

[18] Rothstein, p. 49.

[19] *Ibid.,* pp. 50, 51.

[20] *Ibid.,* p. 52. (Italics supplied.)

[21] *Ibid.,* p. 50.

[22] John A. Carrol and Mary W. Ashworth, *George Washington, First in Peace* (New York: Charles Scribner's Sons, 1957), pp. 640, 641.

[23] Dr. John Brickell, who carefully reviewed George Washington's treatment, estimates that 82 ounces of blood had been withdrawn *(ibid.,* p. 642).

[24] *Ibid.,* p. 643.

[25] Rothstein, pp. 61, 62.

[26] Lyons and Petrucelli, pp. 437, 510, 511, 593.

[27] *Ibid.,* pp. 493, 549-559.

CHAPTER THREE

A Physician Explains . . .

THE DRUGS THAT PHYSICIANS DISPENSED IN ELLEN WHITE'S DAY

From earliest times humanity has sought medications to relieve pain and treat and cure illness and disease. The Chinese long ago compiled herbals, or lists of medicinal plants. The ancient Egyptians, Greeks, and Romans also prepared herbals. During the Middle Ages Avicenna, or Ibn Sina (A.D. 980-1037), known as the "Prince of Physicians" in eastern Persia, methodically codified a whole system of medicine. After the collapse of the Roman Empire certain monastic orders of the Christian church preserved many of the ancient medical treatises. With the advent of the Renaissance (fifteenth and sixteenth centuries) scholars began to reread such writings. Pharmacopeias, or books describing the properties and formulations of medications, with their suggested uses, appeared from time to time in Britain, France, and other European countries.[1]

In general, such books classified medications into two groups: simples opposed to compounds or mixtures of medicines.

Simples

A simple originally referred to a single plant or herb, or an extract of or preparation derived from the herb. But in time people began including minerals in this group, and pharmacologists later added compounds of minerals. To trace the history of the various words we will be considering in this chapter, the reader should consult the *Oxford English Dictionary*.[2] The OED gives either the first known written usage of a specific meaning of a word or a representative example. "Simple," for example, still contains many of its old meanings. This is how Webster has defined the word "simple": (adjective) "Single; uncompounded; uncombined; not blended with something else; elementary; as, a simple substance, color, or medicinal preparation"; (noun) "a: medicinal plant b: a vegetable drug having only one ingredient."

A "simpler" is "one who collects simples or medicinal plants."[3] You will notice that under the definition of "simple," both as an adjective and as a noun, the word may refer to a medicinal agent.

The Dispensing of "Simples"

Many books on medicine and therapeutics published during the early 1800s demonstrate the type of medicine generally practiced then. In this chapter we have selected excerpts from a few such publications to acquaint the reader with how people diagnosed and treated disease during the major portion of Ellen White's lifetime.

One must not forget that the discipline of medicine was changing, though, during those same years. With the emergence of the basic sciences of medicine—anatomy, physiology, biochemistry, microbiology, pathology, and pharmacology—it gradually became evident that illness resulted from either germs causing *infectious diseases* or to alterations in the biochemistry and physiology of body organs producing *noninfectious,* or biological "breakdown" diseases.

E. G. Clarke, M.D., of the Royal College of Physicians of London, wrote *Compendium of the Practice of Physic* in Latin. Later R. W. Worthington, a surgeon of the British Navy who subsequently practiced in Philadelphia, translated it into English (published in 1818). It is interesting to see how it presents two common diseases, giving their causes, diagnoses, and treatments.

"Diabetes, or an immoderate flow of urine.

"*Symptoms.* A great increase in the quantity of urine, at first insipid, afterwards of a sweet taste [determined by tasting], a greenish colour, equalling or exceeding in quantity the aliment introduced [water drunk], constant thirst, sometimes a voracious appetite, dryness of the fauces [mouth and throat], the skin dry and harsh, feet and toes oedematous [swollen with fluid], a burning heat of the skin without the slightest perspiration, hectic fever.

"*Causes.* The causes are all such as debilitate the system, hard drinking, cold applied to the body, excess of venery [sexual activities], too powerful diuretics [agents that increase urine], immoderate evacuations, former diseases: the approximate cause appears to be a diseased state of the stomach impeding the natural powers of digestion and assimilation.

"*Cure.* A diet rich in animal food, vegetables being wholly abstained from; emetics [vomiting agents]; diaphoretics [sweating agents], particularly ipecacuanha [ipecac] and opium; alkaline salts; hydro-sulphuret of ammonia; small blisters applied to the region of the kidneys; mercurial preparations; camphor; astringents, as powdered galls with lime-water; alum; tonics, anointing of the body with oil or some liniment; flannel should be worn next to the skin."[4]

It is hard for us today to comprehend the mind-set of the times. Blistering along with a whole array of powerful drugs would debilitate the patient, thus encouraging the physician to use different and stronger agents. Medical science did not discover insulin until 100 years later. If the type of diabetes was adult onset (Type II), a simple diet, low in fat and high in dietary fiber, would probably have cured the sufferer.

"*Scorbutus or Scurvy.*

"*Symptoms.* Unwonted lassitude; aversion to motion, dejection of the spirits; pale and swollen face, great prostration of strength, faintness after exercise, palpitation of the heart, wandering pains in the muscles are often the first indications of the disease; blood oozes from the gums which are soft and spongy; the breath is highly fetid, the gums ulcerated, the teeth are laid bare and become loose; . . . ulcers break out over the whole of the body; the limbs swell and are painful, . . . in the latter stages haemorrhages break out from various parts of the body, as the mouth, nostrils, rectum and the extremities of the fingers. . . .

"*Causes.* The remote causes are putrescent salted animal food;[5] a want of vegetable substances; want of exercise, cold, moisture, depressing passions of the mind, neglect of cleanliness, the proximate cause is supposed to be a preternaturally saline state of the blood. . . .

"*Cure.* Fresh animal and vegetable food; ripe subacid fruit, fermented liquors; as cider, and malt liquor, strict cleanliness, stimulants, as horseradish, white mustard, etc. wine, preparations of iron, bark [chinchona, source of quinine], mineral acids, opium; for the spongy gums, gargles, composed of a solution of alum . . . cataplasms [poultice] of sorrel should be applied to the ulcers; . . . oxygen gas should also be introduced into the system."[6]

While the medical science of the time prescribed each drug or medicine as a single agent, it dispensed multiple drugs for the same condition. They interacted in the patient's body. Dr. Worthington, a surgeon of the British Navy, published the book cited from above in 1818 in Philadelphia, where he was practicing at the time. Dr. Lind, also of the British Navy, had published in 1753, 65 years earlier than Worthington's book, his *Treatise of the Scurvy.* He had demonstrated that the juice of two limes (or lemons) would cure scurvy. It is difficult to understand why Worthington was still advocating quinine and opium and other worthless procedures. Science isolated vitamin C during the early part of the twentieth century and found it to be the antiscurvy factor. The two limes provided about 40 milligrams of vitamin C.

Mixtures

Historically, medicinal mixtures date back many centuries. Galen, a Greek physician, has been credited as the originator of a mixture called theriac. He, it is believed, made the mixture from some 70-odd substances, including such things as animal tissues, minerals, medicinal herbs, alcohol, etc. Through the centuries other physicians added other ingredients, so by the nineteenth century it contained some 230 ingredients. It was still known as theriac but also as the celebrated *antidote of Mattioli.* In 1830 Claude

Bernard's master advised him that he should not throw away any remedy that he spoiled while compounding a prescription, but should keep it for making theriac! Someone else repeated the same suggestion in 1839![7]

Simply put, mixtures consisted of a number of medicinal herbs or chemicals, or some of both, combined together in some vehicle such as water, alcohol, honey, or sugar syrup. Depending on their strength, physicians prescribed the dose in drops, teaspoonfuls, and so forth.

The Dispensatory of the United States (1849) comments:

"There are certain principles upon which medicines may be advantageously combined. . . .

"Different medicines are very often mixed together, in order to meet different and coexisting indications, without any reference to the influence which they may reciprocally exert on each other. Thus in the same patient we not unfrequently meet with debility of stomach and constipation of the bowels, connected with derangement of the hepatic function. To answer the indications presented by these morbid conditions, we may properly combine in the same dose, a tonic, cathartic, and mercurial alterative. For similar reasons we often unite tonics, purgatives, and emmenagogues, anodynes and diaphoretics, emetics and cathartics, antacids, astringents, and tonics; and scarcely two medicines can be mentioned, not absolutely incompatible with each other, which may not occasionally be combined with advantage to counteract coexisting morbid conditions.

"Another very important object of combination is the modification which is thereby effected in the actions of medicines differing from each other in properties. In this way new powers are sometimes developed, and those previously existing are greatly increased."[8]

I will attempt to put this archaic medical jargon into everyday language. The physician in our example sets up a hypothetical case: the patient has "debility of the stomach, constipation, and hepatic (liver) dysfunction." We would term this impairment or weakness of the stomach (possibly indigestion), constipation or fewer than desired bowel movements, along with some nonspecific problem with the liver.

The writer had no laboratory tests to aid him in his diagnosis. On the basis of external observation alone, he prescribes a tonic to supposedly strengthen or tone up the stomach (not possible), a cathartic to cause bowel movements, and a mercury salt to help the liver (of no benefit, highly toxic, and no longer used).

For the same or similar problems he goes on to state that it would be appropriate simultaneously to prescribe: a *tonic* (a mixture of substances believed to strengthen the body generally); *purgatives,* substances that purge or clean out the intestinal tract; *emmenagogues,* agents that stimulate the uterine muscle and normalize menstruation; *anodynes,* temperature-reducing drugs; *diaphoretics,* sweating agents; *emetics* that cause vomiting; *cathartics* that stimulate bowel movements; *antacids* to neutralize stomach acid; and *astringents* that coagulate, thicken, or decrease mucous secretions.

Can you imagine how you would feel if you were vomiting, alternately sweating and then shivering, saliva flowing from your mouth, coughing up secretions, enduring cramping of your bowels and frequent watery, sometimes bloody stools? And if this was not enough, receiving medicines to dry your mouth, coagulate or thicken your bronchial secretions (windpipe), along with acid-neutralizing agents for anything you might have left in your stomach. And all this happening at one and the same time! Plus, don't forget that the physician was simultaneously draining large amounts of blood from your body. It is absolutely unbelievable when we contrast it with how medical science would treat you today.

The example we have cited was written in 1849. No wonder Ellen White, joining with other reformers, wrote in 1864 that "the endless variety of medicines in the market, the numerous advertisements of new drugs and mixtures, all of which, as they say, do wonderful cures, kill hundreds where they benefit one. Those who are sick are not patient. They will take various medicines, some of which are very powerful, although they know nothing of the nature of the mixtures. All the medicines they take only make their recovery more hopeless. Yet they keep dosing, and continue to grow weaker, until they die. Some will have medicine at all events.

Then let them take these hurtful mixtures and the various deadly poisons upon their own responsibility. God's servants should not administer medicines which they know will leave behind injurious effects upon the system, even if they do relieve present suffering" ([1864] 4SG 139, 140).

In 1893 she added: "Practitioners are very much in earnest in using their dangerous concoctions, and I am decidedly opposed to resorting to such things" (letter 17a, 1893, 2SM 279).

And four years later she continued: "The treatment we gave when the sanitarium was first established required earnest labor to combat disease. We did not use drug concoctions; we followed hygienic methods. This work was blessed of God" (letter 81, 1892, *ibid.*, 293).

Perhaps another illustration, taken from a text written 25 years later, will further emphasize the continued use of mixtures. The book *Universal Formulary*, published in 1874, in discussing the preparation and administration of various remedies explains:

"Powders—These are of two kinds: *simple* and *compound*. The first are prepared by pulverization; and the second by the mixture of two or more simple powders, except where one of the ingredients is employed to facilitate the more minute division of the others, as in the case of the powder of ipecacuanha and opium."[9]

We need to remember that modern laboratory methods of diagnosing disease were nonexistent. As pointed out earlier, medical science of the time classified only symptoms, and employed such categories to designate specific "diseases." It was therefore very tempting, when uncertainty existed as to what precisely the patient was suffering from, to use several medications or pre-prepared mixtures of drugs. If one did not work, another might! Unfortunately, physicians too often ignored the mounting toxicity of such combinations.

When I took medicine from 1937 to 1941 at what is now the Loma Linda University School of Medicine, my pharmacology instructors kept emphasizing that we, as future physicians, should use "a rifle, not a shotgun" in prescribing medicines, meaning, of course, that we should employ a single agent rather than a number of agents. At the time tonics, a mixture of a number of medicinals, were still quite popular, and remained so until the advent of multivitamin and mineral preparations (c. 1947). Vitamin and mineral supplements, as we well know, are mixtures of many highly potent chemicals, which, while being essential to life, can in either too small or too large amounts produce profound and harmful effects within our bodies. And today we face an added concern—the free and unbridled use of medicinal herbs (vegetable or botanic drugs). While they do have potential for good, they can also cause grave harm.

It is hard for us today to understand what "drug medication" or "drugging" was really like and what Ellen White and other reformers were referring to when they used the terms. A careful and thoughtful consideration of the following examples from nineteenth-century American medicine should further illustrate why reform in therapeutics and the way physicians medically treated patients was so essential.

How Drugs Were Used for Various Illnesses

The 1896 *Reference Book of Practical Therapeutics* has this listing: "*Sclerosis* of internal organs, especially the liver and kidneys, may be retarded by the persistent use of gold and sodium chloride. . . . A solution of the homides of gold and arsenic [Auri Arsenas] has been successfully employed for several years.[10]

Sclerosis was a term used for a whole spectrum of diseased conditions of body organs. The reference book above mentions ones involving the liver, the lungs, and the kidneys. It names a number of problems of the nervous system: neuritis, locomotor ataxia, sciatica, epilepsy and senile degenerative changes, and neurotic disease (Alzheimer's and possibly a spinal disc?). It also lists swelling of the lymph glands in the neck, arthritis, a stage of syphilis, and inflammation of the iris of the eye. Yet it wants to treat all these diverse conditions with two poisonous substances, gold and arsenic!

A System of Practical Therapeutics, published in 1897, says that pernicious anemia is "best treated by careful and nourishing feeding and by arsenic and iron. Arsenic is the drug on which experience has taught us to place most reliance. Its mode of action is not understood, but the most probable explanation is that it stimulates the formation of new corpuscles by the red bone-marrow."[11]

Medicine employed the word "pernicious" for this form of anemia because it was, until the turn of the century, universally fatal. Arsenic, as is well known, is a highly toxic chemical with no beneficial effect. Iron would be of little, if any, help. Early in the twentieth century liver, and later liver extracts, proved beneficial. In 1949 researchers isolated the missing agent resulting in pernicious anemia from liver extracts and named it vitamin B_{12}. The amount needed to satisfactorily maintain a patient suffering from such anemia is as low as one microgram (one millionth of a quarter of a teaspoonful) per day!

One book offered the following remedies for dealing with thirst:

1. Desire for cold water: arsenic; Peruvian bark (quinine); sabadilla (a drastic emetic and cathartic).

2. Great desire for cold drinks: dulcamara (bittersweet; causes nausea and vomiting); euphorbium (a harsh emetic and cathartic); marsh tea (used as a sweating agent).

3. Thirst for cold drinks, particularly water: soluble mercury.

4. Great thirst for cold drinks in the evening, without heat: bismuth.

5. Unquenchable thirst, particularly for cold drinks: veratrum (swamp hellebore, Indian poke, both nauseants).

6. Great desire for cold drinks without heat (fever): belladonna (atropine; dries the mouth).

7. No thirst for many days: manganese.

8. No thirst: lycopodium (club moss, used for diseases of kidneys).

9. Drinks less than usual: staphysagria (stavesacre, a violent emetic and cathartic).

10. No thirst or else it is excessive: camphor.

11. Absence of thirst, with heat in the whole body: hydrochloric acid.[12]

While the preceding material comes from a homeopathic book, regular physicians prescribed similar therapy. When you consider the above prescriptions of arsenic, mercury, atropine, camphor, quinine—all given for simple thirst—you begin to realize the enormity of the problem of drug use. The various medications caused diarrhea, vomiting, sweating, drying of the mouth, along with burning in the stomach and cramping of the bowels. Today medical staff give water by mouth or water containing minerals and glucose (electrolyte solutions) by vein in almost all serious accidents or illnesses, let alone for a patient who complains of thirst!

At the time physicians restricted water for many illnesses, Ellen White spoke out against the practice. In 1865 she wrote: "They [the sick] died victims to their own ignorance, and that of their friends, and the ignorance and deception of physicians, who gave them fashionable poisons, and would not allow them pure water to drink, and fresh air to breathe, to invigorate the vital organs, purify the blood, and help nature in her task in overcoming the bad conditions of the system. These valuable remedies which Heaven has provided, without money and without price, were cast aside, and considered not only as worthless, but even as dangerous enemies, while poisons, prescribed by physicians, were in blind confidence taken" (*Health, Or, How to Live,* No. 4, 1865, pp. 55, 56, quoted in 2SM 456).

"Go with me to yonder sickroom," she said in 1882. "There lies a husband and father, a man who is a blessing to society and to the cause of God. He has been suddenly stricken down by disease. The fire of fever seems consuming him. He longs for pure water to moisten the parched lips, to quench the raging thirst, and cool the fevered brow. But, no; the doctor has forbidden water. The stimulus of strong drink is given and adds fuel to the fire. The blessed, heaven-sent water, skillfully applied, would quench the devouring flame; but it is set aside for poisonous drugs" (5T 195 [1882]).

The nineteenth century treated whooping cough with ipecac. When given in large doses the resulting vomiting appeared to stop the paroxysms of coughing. Medical doctors also prescribed ipecac for such diverse conditions as asthma, chronic bronchitis, and dysentery.[13] Ipecac is an excellent agent to induce vomiting, and medicine still uses it for this purpose in cases of swallowed poisons, but certainly not for the conditions listed above.

When threatened by cholera, George B. Wood stated that "among the remedies best calculated to meet the above indications are opium and calomel, in small and frequently repeated doses, combined, when the discharges are copious, with acetate of lead, and, in addition, if this should prove insufficient, with tannic acid, kino, catechu, or the extract of rhatany. . . . The mutual reaction of these substances, though resulting in the formation of new compounds, does not by any means necessarily imply a therapeutical incompatibility."[14]

What Wood did not know was that opium with its alkaloids, morphine and codeine, has a constipating effect, while calomel is a potent cathartic agent producing an opposite action. For a time medicine believed that lead acetate or sugar of lead was beneficial in certain diarrheas, but then discontinued its use because of serious and often fatal poisoning. Tannic acid, an astringent, tends to shrink tissues, and physicians employed it in diarrheas, hoping to coat the intestinal wall with a layer of coagulated mucus. Kino, a juice obtained from the bark of a number of tropical trees; catechu, extracted from the leaves and twigs of the gambir plant; and rhatany or Peruvian rhatany, obtained from the krameria root, are all powerful astringents employed to treat diarrhea.

Cholera actually results from a toxin released by the cholera germs (bacilli). Vomiting and a massive watery diarrhea soon dehydrate the sufferer. To save the victim's life, one must rapidly administer large amounts of intravenous fluids (10-plus liters during the first 24 hours). Fluid replacement alone will save the sufferer, but an antibiotic will accelerate the recovery. A vaccine will give reasonable protection for about six months. How different is medicine today.

Speaking of the disease typhus, an 1862 medical book suggested "administering a full dose of calomel, sulphate of magnesia, or sulphate of soda, all in large and repeated doses, according to age and other circumstances. The calomel was generally given in a dose of 10 to 20 grains every day or every second day, until the fetid odour of the dejections was gone."[15]

The reader will recall that physicians mentioned in the previous chapter believed that the application of blisters would be an effective treatment. Here the author wants the patient's colon scoured by repeated doses of strong cathartics!

Thomas Watson suggested how to treat nonspecific fever: "In the outset of the disease, and while its species may as yet be uncertain, if the bowels have not been already purged by nature or by art, it will be right to give three or four grains of calomel [mercury cathartic] at once, and to follow up this dose by a senna draught [another cathartic]. After that, in the earlier period of the fever, especially if the alvine [belly and intestines] discharges are scanty, dark-coloured, or otherwise of unnatural appearance, a couple of grains of calomel, or four or five grains of the *hydrargyrum cum cretâ* [mercury with chalk], may very properly be prescribed, in pills, three or four times a day. . . . Should the diarrhea persist, or become profuse, a certain quantity of Dover's powder [a mixture of ipecac, which causes vomiting, and opium], or of the extract of poppy [opium], should be added to the hydrargyrum cum cretâ."[16]

The cathartics (mercurial and hydrargyrum, both no longer used today) are powerful, and medical doctors gave them in large and frequent doses, often causing bloody stools. Opium and its derivatives produce constipation, and as stated above, attempted to reduce the diarrhea triggered by the cathartics.

The *Manual of Practical Therapeutics* offered as a treatment of asthma hydrocyanic (prussic) acid or hydrogen cyanide. At the time medical science believed that it relieved "catarrhous suffocations," and the "oppressed state of the pulmonary circulation." Physicians also used it for consumption (tuberculosis of the lungs), bronchitis, pneumonia, and pleurisy.[17] But cyanide in any form is an extremely poisonous substance and has no usefulness as a medicinal agent. It kills by blocking the oxygen the cells need, and it would be hard to find anything that would be worse for asthma.

J. M. Fothergill in *The Practitioner's Handbook of Treatment, or the Principles of Therapeutics* outlined "the various measures by which we act upon the nervous system, and the means by which we can control that system, or excite action in it, when it becomes desirable to do so. . . . Of the neurotic agents which diminish action in the nervous system, opium, chloral hydrate, and bromide of potassium are chief in common use; calabar bean [picrotoxin], conium [hemlock], and others are potent, but not so commonly resorted to; while hyoscyamus, camphor, etc., are less powerful, except in doses far beyond those of the pharmacopoeia, and are chiefly used as adjuncts to other remedies. Another class of agents, as belladonna [atropine] and cannabis indica [marijuana], lie across the borderland of depressant and excitant neurotics, and had best be considered under the latter heading."[18]

Opium has a sedative action, as do chloral hydrate (it has an obnoxious taste) and bromides that act more slowly. Picrotoxin, found in calabar beans, is a powerful convulsant, as is hemlock. Hyoscyamus and camphor are highly poisonous substances, while beladonna, or atropine, and marijuana may cause psychotic conditions.

All the above agents were highly toxic whether used singly or in combination with others, yet physicians gave them in large and frequent doses. When we contemplate the many purposes for which each substance was supposedly effective, we shudder. Ellen White attacked this unintelligent and dangerous use of drugs in no uncertain terms. She wisely condemned such medical practice and urged that both physicians and patients should discard such substances, commenting in 1864 that "more deaths have been caused by drug-taking than from all other causes combined. If there was in the land one physician in the place of thousands, a vast amount of premature mortality would be prevented. Multitudes of physicians, and multitudes of drugs, have cursed the inhabitants of the earth, and have carried thousands and tens of thousands to untimely graves" (4SG 133).

Multiple Uses of a Drug

Another example of how physicians employed a single drug for all kinds of problems is that of aconite, a drug derived from the tuberous root of common monkshood. Sydney Ringer claimed in 1869 that "of all the drugs we possess, there are certainly none more valuable than aconite. Its virtues by most persons are only beginning to be appreciated, but it is not difficult to foresee that in a short time it will be most extensively employed in the diseases immediately to be noticed." He called it useful in "neuralgias of the brow or face" effective in controlling inflammation, such as tonsillitis or acute sore throat. "Large, livid, red, glazed, and dry tonsils may often in 24 hours have their appearance completely altered," he wrote. "[Aconite's] effects on catarrhal croup are conspicuous. . . . The effects of this valuable drug . . . are equally important on pneumonia, pleurisy, and the graver inflammations."[19]

Aconite is a rapidly acting and powerful poison. Toxic levels characteristically produce a peculiar numbness in the lips and mouth, then in the fingers. The heart beats weakly, and respiration slows with stupor or convulsions preceding death.[20]

Another drug nineteenth-century medical science touted was balsam of copaiva, or copaiba, a "stimulant of mucous membranes generally, particularly that of the genito-urinary system. . . . In some persons, Copaiba, even in small doses, produces violent vomiting and purging. . . . A long course of Copaiba is not unattended with danger. . . . Urticaria . . . is by no means an unusual sequence of this remedy."[21] Urticaria, a red raised rash of hands and feet, often spread rapidly over the whole body. Itching was extreme. Because of these and other toxic reactions, the drug is no longer used. It was, however, in common use for gonorrhea, hemorrhoids or piles, diseases of the heart, as well as croup, psoriasis, smallpox, and scarlet fever.

The *Manual of Practical Therapeutics* prescribed strychnos nux vomica (strychnine) for a wide variety of ailments, including rheumatism, paralysis, amaurosis (gradual loss of sight), night blindness, epilepsy, nervous exhaustion, and intestinal obstructions.[22] Strychnine is ineffective in these ailments. It is an extremely poisonous substance, and even in small doses caused multiple deaths.

By the late 1930s, when I studied to be a doctor, medicine no longer used strychnine. After I graduated and while I was a first-year surgical resident at the College of Medical Evangelists, word got around about a patient in the medical unit with strychnine poisoning. I made it a point to see the person.

When I arrived at the door of the private room, the nurse warned me not to make any sound. Heavy drapes placed over the window darkened the room. In the gloom I made out the patient. Then the engineer of a passing train blew his whistle. The patient went into a massive convulsion. Strychnine seems to sensitize all the nerve pathways that respond to sound.

Some years later (1951) my wife and I were on our way to Salt Lake City, driving a less-traveled road. It was late afternoon, and a cold wind was blowing. From the corner of my eye I spotted an automobile with all four wheels in the air. For a moment I thought it was an old wreck. Then my wife said, "I think I saw someone near the wreck. You had better turn around to see if you can be of any help."

Quickly I noticed an elderly woman covering a body with a piece of cardboard. I got out, as did my wife. The cold wind struck us, and the cold went to our bones. The woman was the wife of a well-digger camped beyond a hill on the opposite side of the road. She had heard the noise of the accident and had come to give help.

Mentioning to her that I was a physician, I asked if I could do anything. With a confident smile she replied, "I'm a nurse and have just given both of them a good shot of strychnine. It's a great medicine, and I wouldn't do without it. I always carry some with me in case I need it, like now." Just then the older of the two victims died. The younger man was having trouble breathing. He had a head injury, and blood was running out of his nose and ears. She had already asked a passing motorist to alert the local sheriff.

Within minutes the sheriff arrived in a station wagon. He and his helpers lifted the living victim into the rear of the station wagon that served as a makeshift ambulance. They thanked the woman, said they would be back, and drove off. My wife and I walked over to the wrecked car. All its doors had flown open, scattering the contents of the car across the desert floor. Balanced precariously on the underside of the roof (the car was upside down) was an open half-full bottle of whiskey. As we walked toward the road we could see the holes made in the ground as the car had gone end over end two or three times. It was the last time I heard of anyone using strychnine as a medicine.

References

[1] Fielding H. Garrison, *An Introduction to the History of Medicine* (Philadelphia: W. B. Saunders Co., 1929), p. 289.

[2] *The Oxford English Dictionary: Being a Corrected Re-Issue With an Introduction, Supplement, and Bibliography of a New English Dictionary of Historical Principles Founded Mainly on the Material Collected by the Philological Society* (Oxford, Eng.: Claredon Press, 1933; reprinted 1961). The OED is also available on the Internet.

[3] For further discussion, see chapter on simple remedies.

[4] E. G. Clarke, *Compendium of the Practice of Physic*, trans. from Latin by R. W. Worthington (Philadelphia: James Webster, 1818), pp. 151-153.

[5] Scurvy was a common disease of sailors, especially on long voyages. Animal foods would putrefy, as no refrigeration existed. The usual diet of a sailor was hardtack (a dry, hard biscuit), meat of some kind (usually dry), and a ration of grog (rum).

[6] Clarke, pp. 183-185.

[7] Charles Singer and Ashworth E. Underwood, *A Short History of Medicine*, 2nd ed. (New York: Oxford Press, 1962), p. 676.

[8] Arthur Osol and George Farmer, *Dispensatory of the United States of America*, 24th ed. (Philadelphia: J. B. Lippincott Co., 1849), pp. 1316, 1317.

[9] Robert Eglesfeld and John Michael Maisch, *Universal Formulary Official and Other Medicines*, ed. John Michael (Philadelphia: Henry C. Lea, 1874), p. 639.

[10] *Reference Book of Practical Therapeutics*, ed. Frank P. Foster (New York: Appleton and Co., 1896), p. 454.

[11] *A System of Practical Therapeutics*, ed. Hobart M. Hare (Philadelphia: Lea Brothers & Co., 1897), Vol. IV, p. 425.

[12] E. E. Marcy and F. W. Hunt, *The Homeopathic Theory and Practice of Medicine* (New York: William Radde, 1866), Vol. I, pp. 255, 256.

[13] *Manual of Practical Therapeutics*, pp. 387-389.

[14] Wood, *A Treatise on the Practice of Medicine*, Vol. I, p. 694.

[15] John Hjalletin, "On the Disinfecting Treatment of Typhus, Eruptive and Enteric," *Edinburgh Medical Journal* VIII (1862): 230, 231.

[16] Thomas Watson, *Lectures on the Principles and Practice of Physic* (Philadelphia: Blanchard and Lea, 1858), p. 1118.

[17] *Manual of Practical Therapeutics*, pp. 364, 365.

[18] J. M. Fothergill, *The Practitioner's Handbook of Treatment*, or the *Principles of Therapeutics* (Philadelphia: Lead Febiger).

[19] Sydney Ringer, "Papers on the Therapeutic Action of Drugs," *Lancet* 1 (1869): 42-44.

[20] Joseph P. Remington and Horatio C. Wood, *The Dispensatory of the United States of America*, 20th ed. (Philadelphia: J. B. Lippincott, 1918), p. 89.

[21] *Manual of Practical Therapeutics*, pp. 243, 244.

[22] *Ibid.*, pp. 616-619.

CHAPTER FOUR

A Physician Explains . . .

DRUGS DEFINED

SECTION I

What Is a Drug and How Does It Work?

From its beginning humanity has sought relief from suffering and cure from disease. Through the centuries people discovered various substances they believed to be of help. In different countries and times medicines have come from a great variety of sources. Here are a few examples.

The human race has derived medicines from such plants as the foxglove, the poppy, and chinchona bark; from animal parts, including the horn of the rhino, the fat of a bear, the blood and bile of a snake; and from the earth: for example, arsenic, mercury, and bismuth. As a boy growing up in northeast India I became aware that people considered bear's fat a certain cure for rheumatism and that the ground-up horn of a hornbill would relieve intestinal problems. If the reader ever has the opportunity to visit Taipei, Taiwan, I would recommend a trip to the snake market. There customers can drink the blood and bile of whatever snake they select.

Professor Leslie Benet, currently chair of the Department of Pharmacy, School of Pharmacy, University of California, Berkeley, declares that "a *drug* is broadly defined as any chemical agent that affects processes of living."[1] Since drugs are chemicals that modify the "processes of living," it would help us to understand what they are and how they function. That will enable us to more clearly grasp what a drug is and how it works.

How Our Bodies Function

The human body consists of trillions of cells, each genetically a different type designed for a specific purpose. We have discrete skin cells, bone cells, muscle cells, liver cells, and brain cells, just to mention a few. Organized into specialized groups, they make our skin, bones, muscles, brain, and other organs.

How do our bodies accomplish the various functions that keep us alive and allow us to engage in our everyday activities? Activities such as, dressing, walking, eating, writing, digesting food, throwing a ball, and watching the face of a loved one? While we are aware of some of these obvious functions, we are completely oblivious to hundreds, doubtless thousands, of others hidden from our view. For example, how do certain cells of the pancreas produce insulin? Why do muscles contract? How do liver cells make bile? How does the mucous membrane of the stomach manufacture hydrochloric acid and not be dissolved by it? And how is a molecule of hemoglobin, the oxygen-carrying red pigment in blood cells, fabricated? In a living organism all this happens because of millions upon millions of complex biochemical activities proceeding at incredible speeds within the cells that compose the tissues and organs of our bodies.

A cell is a tiny chemical factory that does the work assigned to it. In each cell specifically designed protein molecules called enzymes perform one highly specialized task. Since it requires a number of steps to manufacture a product such as insulin or hemoglobin, the cell has the various enzymes arranged in a well-organized assembly line. Each enzyme performs its single operation and then passes what it has produced on to the next stage, until the substance is complete. Scientists refer to such assembly lines as enzyme systems. A diagram of the hemoglobin assembly line appears on the following page.

Each cell has an outside covering called a cell membrane. The membrane has ports or gates through which substances may enter the cell. Other enzymes or port keepers on the outside surface control the gates, opening or closing them. Receptors on the surface of the cell act like locks, requiring the correct keys, or regulators, to ac-

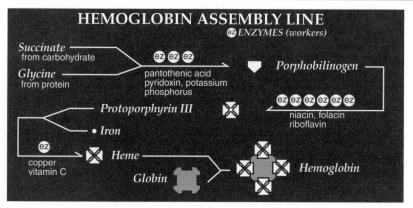

Fig. 1. The cell uses succinate and glycine to form one molecule of porphobilinogen. Then the cell arranges four molecules of porphobilinogen into a molecule of protoporphyrin III. An atom of iron is next added to form heme. A molecule of globin arrives from another enzyme assembly line and four molecules of heme attach themselves to it, forming a molecule of hemoglobin.

tivate them. Once attached to the receptor, the regulator can, from the outside, influence the operations inside the cell.

How Do Cells Regulate Themselves?

Regulating cells is a highly complex process, and science does not yet understand all the mechanisms involved. However, we will look at some analogies of how such processes might work.

Just as we control the speed of a car by the use of the brake or accelerator, so a "brake" or "accelerator" affects the rate or speed an enzyme or enzyme system operates. The regulators of an enzyme or enzyme system consist of a large array of substances, such as hormones, neurotransmitters, certain minerals, and many other chemical compounds. Howard Kutchai, a cellular physiologist, discussing the regulatory substances and how they modify the activity inside cells, states that "some regulatory substances, such as steroid hormones, enter the cell and influence the transcription of certain genes. Many regulatory substances, however, exert their effects from outside the cell. The first step in the action of such substances is to bind to specific receptors in the plasma [cell] membrane."[2]

Now let's try to explain what can happen in a cell by again using a car as a model. You, the regulator, sit down behind the steering wheel. You insert the ignition key in the lock (receptor) on your steering column and switch on your engine. Now, although you are free to do a number of things, you are also limited in other ways. Your running engine will not allow you to fly like an airplane or to cruise on a lake like a boat. It can do only what its manufacturer designed it to do. But you, the regulator, can travel down the road using your brake and accelerator to modify the rate at which the engine runs and the speed at which you travel. You can speed up, slow down, or stop.

In a similar way drugs can speed up, slow down, or stop the chemical or enzyme activities of cells. Dr. Elliott Ross, of the University of Texas, discussing the functions of medications, brings out this point when he states that "a drug potentially is capable of altering the rate at which any bodily function proceeds. . . . Drugs do not create effects, but instead modulate functions."[3] What Dr. Ross is saying is that a chemical, whether it be a hormone, mineral, medicinal herb, or some medicine or drug, does not change how an enzyme works, but only the rate or speed at which it operates.

How a Drug Works

Now let us go to the dictionary to learn how it defines the word "medicine." According to Webster, "medicine" is "any substance or preparation used in treating a disease." If we now look for the meaning of "drug," we find the following:

"Any substance used as a medicine, or in making medicines, for internal or external use," and "any substance or mixture of substances intended to be used for the cure, mitigation, or prevention of disease of either man or other animals."[4]

So it becomes evident that "drug" or "medicine" constitute one and the same thing and refer to any substance or chemical, whether an anti-cancer agent or an antibiotic, a medicinal herb or a synthetic chemical, a hormone or an anti-malarial—all, when used to prevent or cure illness and disease, fall into the category of a medicine or drug. It is the way the health professionals and the laity at large use the words "medicines" or "drugs." They employ them interchangeably.

Enzymes and enzyme systems do the body's work. The cells are the factories that house them. The chemical or chemicals that make up the medicine must influence these enzymes. They do so either by entering the cell through a port in the cell membrane or by attaching to a receptor on its surface. At times they may diffuse through the cell membrane. But whatever the way, they modify the activities within the cell.

Each natural biochemical regulator in the body has part of its molecule shaped like a "key" to fit its special receptor. Drugs may act as regulators of cell function in a similar manner. Like normal physiological regulators, drugs are also chemicals and have shapes. When a certain part of the drug molecule has the same shape as does the "key" of a physiological regulator, it will latch onto that receptor.

In a failing heart, for example, the muscle fibers of the heart have stretched until the flabby heart walls cannot contract enough to effectively squeeze out the blood from the heart chambers. The botanic drug foxglove or its purified active ingredient, the glycoside digoxin, will affect certain enzymes in the cells of the heart muscle so the muscle fibers shorten in length. Now when the heart contracts it pumps the blood more efficiently.[5]

The pneumococcus, the germ responsible for a common form of pneumonia, has a membrane or capsule surrounding it that protects it against the body's defenses, the soldier cells, or phagocytes. Penicillin attacks the enzyme systems of the coccus that make the capsule, resulting in a weak or sometimes incomplete capsule. The body's phagocytes can now more easily destroy the coccus (plural cocci).[6]

What Determines the Effectiveness of a Drug?

A number of factors determine how well a drug works: its chemical shape, how well its shape fits the shape of a receptor, the number of receptors present in the tissues, and how many receptors are actually available for the drug molecules to attach to.[7]

This leads us to the matter of *dose,* that is, the amount of a medicine taken. In any given person a small dose will give a small or shorter response than will a larger dose, an effect called the dose-response relationship. If we continually reduce the dose, the response will be less and less until finally nothing happens at all. The drug must reach a minimum concentration, called the threshold level, before the drug will have any effect. The drug will not work below the threshold level, or minimum dose. If, on the other hand, we continually increase the dose, it will in time become toxic.

We should emphasize that these principles apply not only to drugs but to vitamins, minerals, hormones, medicinal herbs (botanic drugs), or any other chemical substances in the body.

The way or route a drug enters the body will influence its effectiveness. The chemical properties of the medicine will determine how it can be given. The most common route is by mouth if the drug is not too irritating, or if it is not destroyed in the stomach, intestine, or liver. The body will absorb some drugs when we place them under the tongue. The physician may introduce others by enema or injection in the vein, muscle, or under the skin. Still others we may inhale or absorb through the skin. Each route determines how fast it reaches its target, what its concentration will be when it gets there, and how long it will remain at its effective concentration. The concentration also depends on how rapidly the body degrades it or how rapidly the kidneys excrete it.[8]

Why Do People Differ in Their Response to Drugs?

We are all genetically different. Just as resistance to disease varies from one person to another, and even from one time to another, so responses to medications vary. My wife's skin is highly sensitive to mercury or any compound of mercury, even to a dilution of one to 10 million parts! She is also sensitive to wood (methyl) alcohol. Neither bothers me.

Let us imagine two friends named Bob and Jack. Bob decides to take a medicine to help him sleep. Jack decides to do the same thing, employing the same medicine in the same dose and at the same time. Sleeping well, Bob gets up in the morning refreshed. On the other hand, Jack does not awaken till sometime in the afternoon. When he does, he is befuddled and feels groggy when he tries to walk. Why the difference?

A number of possible reasons could have affected each man's response to the medicine. Bob's liver broke down the drug, making it easy for his kidneys to eliminate the by-products. Because Jack's liver lacked the ability, his kidneys had to excrete the unmodified drug, taking longer and extending his sleep. Or Jack's kidneys, because of an earlier infection, had less ability to eliminate the drug or its by-products. As a result, the drug remained in his blood for a longer period. It is quite possible that if Jack had received a smaller dose, the results in the two friends might have been the same.

Why Do Drugs Cause Unexpected Effects?

Histamine, a normal constituent of the body, will illustrate the way a physiological regulator, and later its antagonist (a drug), works. Mast cells in the tissues mainly manufacture and store histamine, though to a lesser extent basophil cells, present in the blood, will also make it. Medical research has extensively studied at least two types of histamine receptors, namely H_1 and H_2. H_1 receptors are present in the walls of the bronchi (windpipes) and of the intestines, and when stimulated cause constriction and contraction of the two organs. H_2 receptors, on the other hand, line the stomach wall, and when activated increase the flow of gastric secretions. The walls of the small blood vessels contain both types, and when stimulated cause the walls to dilate and become porous.[9]

When bacteria, chemicals, or a laceration injures the body's tissues, the latter release controlled amounts of histamine. Should you cut your finger or scrape your knee the released histamine causes the small blood vessels to dilate and to become porous. Plasma and proteins, including fibrinogen, escape into the injured tissues. The fibrinogen and proteins clot, the body's way of walling off the injured surfaces so germs cannot enter, and at the same time stop the bleeding and initiate healing.

Again, when a bee stings you and the chemicals in the venom

seep into the tissues, it releases histamine in a similar scenario.

Now let us picture another, more serious, event. When a person highly sensitive or allergic to bee venom gets stung, certain of the toxins (chemicals) in the bee venom trigger a massive release of histamine. Molecules of histamine flood the tissues and attach to their receptors. Vessel walls dilate and become porous. Fluids pour out of the blood into the tissues, causing edema (swelling). The person feels flushed, the skin reddens, and massive hives may appear with intense itching. Swelling of the tongue, larynx, and the air passages of the lungs may accompany it. The blood pressure may drop, and the person may experience nausea, vomiting, cramps, and diarrhea. The individual should go to an emergency room and the care of a physician. The immediate treatment is to give epinephrine (adrenaline), together with antihistamines, by mouth. The physician may also administer steroids.

How an Antihistamine Works

The antihistamine molecules, which partially resemble the shape of histamine molecules, attach themselves to the histamine receptors (mainly H_1, see above). This results in a competition for the receptor sites. Flooding the bloodstream with hundreds of thousands of antihistamine molecules allows them to outnumber those of histamine. By taking over the receptor sites, the antihistamines effectively block the histamine molecules from attaching to them. Unattached histamine then physiologically degrades (breaks down). In this way the antihistamine prevents or minimizes the hives, hay fever, asthma, and possibly anaphylactic shock and death.

When the dose of bee venom is small or the individual has a resistance to the sting, a mild allergic response may occur with itching, local redness and swelling, or possibly a mild attack of hay fever.

Molecules of different chemicals have different shapes. Some are relatively simple while others are highly complex. All the chemicals naturally present in our bodies are so shaped that they interact only with receptors for which they are specifically designed. That prevents unwanted responses. When a substance not normally a constituent of the body, such as an antihistamine, enters the bloodstream and passes into the tissue fluids, its shape resembles only in part the natural histamine molecule. The conforming part attaches to the target histamine receptor and accomplishes the purpose for which the patient took the drug. However, another part of the antihistamine molecule interacts with other unwanted receptors, for example, on the cells of the salivary glands and on certain neurons in the brain. It causes dryness of the mouth and drowsiness, producing what we call side effects.

Other Ways Drugs Cause Problems

Now let's go back to the model of your car that we used when discussing how regulators work. However, we will change it a little. It is a dark night, and for some reason, while you were in a store, the lights that usually illuminate the parking lot have gone out. You exit the store and grope your way to where you left your car. Opening the door, you slide behind the steering wheel, feel for the spot where the ignition key fits, and insert the key. But the lock will not turn. And what is worse, the key has jammed in the ignition. Just then the lights of the parking lot come on, and you find yourself sitting in someone else's car.

Putting the key into the wrong ignition can cause a lot of trouble. So too, a drug's molecular shape may be such that it may jam certain cell receptors, inactivate enzymes on the cell membrane, or, passing through a port in the cell wall, raise havoc from within the cell. Such adverse responses may be minor or they can be extremely severe.

The treatment of epilepsy has long employed the drug phenytoin (Dilantin). When it reacts with the proper target receptors in the brain, it controls the seizures (convulsions). It is not uncommon to observe swelling of the gums and loosening of the teeth, a kind of "localized scurvy" that one can cure with vitamin C.[10] But on occasion it can have more serious adverse effects.

When a medical person administers penicillin to a patient suffering from pneumonia, the penicillin molecules target receptors on the pneumococcus bacilli. The antibiotic is generally highly successful in its mission. While adverse reactions are not common, they do occur, though. The most frequent are allergic reactions, such as hives and fever, though more serious responses may occasionally crop up.[11]

Summary

At any moment, within and around the cells of our bodies, a bewildering array of extremely complex chemical processes are taking place at incredible speeds. They give us life and allow us to function. Both regular and botanic drugs will affect them, their chemical shapes allowing them to behave as regulators influencing either the cell's external or internal chemistry. Usually their effect on the organ or system we want to treat is beneficial. Other parts of the drug molecule, though, may interfere with cell processes elsewhere in the body, resulting in adverse or even toxic responses.

The action of a drug or medicinal herb depends on its concentration in and around the cells of the target organ or body system. The dose, or amount of drug taken, determines the concentration. Also how the patient takes it, whether by mouth, injection, or inhaled, will influence the concentration as well as how rapidly the body breaks it down and expels it. The drug must be at a certain concentration or threshold level to trigger a response. At this level it may have no unwanted side effects, or they may be mild, moderate, or severe.

Beneficial medicines that rarely if ever have adverse responses enjoy wide use. Others that have many widespread toxic reactions are rarely used except for life-destroying diseases, such as cancer and HIV.

As we saw earlier, a drug is a chemical that modifies the activities of cells when used in the prevention, treatment, or cure of a disease. It may be present in the tissues of a plant (medicinal herb), extracted from a medicinal plant, exist as a naturally occurring chemical, or be one that human beings have synthesized. But was that what Ellen White called drugs? We must let her define her own use of the word.

SECTION II

Ellen White Defines What She Considered a Drug

The question as to what Ellen White considered a drug has been a point of contention not only among the Adventist medical profession but also among ordinary church members. At times the arguments as to what is and what is not a drug have generated considerable heat. But the question is a real one, and we need to find an answer. It is not what you or I think she meant by the word "drug," but what she herself identified as a "drug" that is important.

As the discovery of the Rosetta Stone enabled archaeologists to understand the hieroglyphics of ancient Egypt, so a letter written to Ellen White and her response to it provide, I believe, the key to what she meant when she used the word "drug."

A Remarkable Inquiry

Let us examine the letter Edgar Caro sent to Ellen White and her reply to him. On August 15, 1893, Caro, a third-year medical student,[12] wrote to Ellen White for himself and fellow students to find out more clearly what she considered a drug. They had read her comments on the nonuse of drugs in the *Testimonies* and in the book *How to Live,* and they accepted the counsel given as coming from the Lord.

"Several of the students are in doubt as to the meaning of the word 'drug' as mentioned in *How to Live,*" he said. "Does it refer only to the stronger medicines as mercury, strychnine, arsenic, and such poisons, the things we medical students call 'drugs,' or does it also include the simpler remedies, as potassium, iodine, squills, etc.? We know that our success will be proportionate to our adherence to God's methods. For this reason I have asked the above question" (Edgar Caro letter, 1893, quoted in 2SM 278).

You will observe that in his letter Caro inquires about two classes of medicinals: stronger medicines or drugs, as he and the medical students called them, and simpler medicines. He uses the adjective only when asking about the stronger medicines or drugs. Which did she have in mind in her comments in *How to Live?* Now the question we should ask is the same question that Caro raised: When Ellen used the word "drug" or "drugs," did she have in mind only a group of "stronger medicines" or "drugs" as he and the medical students called them, or was she also using the word to include the "simpler remedies"? The dictionary defines the adverb "only" as meaning "solely, exclusively."[13]

An Equally Remarkable Reply

Obviously Caro was trying to be very specific in his inquiry. Ellen White's reply is equally precise.

"Your questions, I will say, are answered largely, if not definitely, in *How to Live.* Drug poisons mean the articles which you have mentioned. The simpler remedies are less harmful in proportion to their simplicity; but in very many cases these are used when not at all necessary. There are simple herbs and roots that every family may use for themselves and need not call a physician any sooner than they would call a lawyer. I do not think that I can give you any definite line of medicines compounded and dealt out by doctors, that are perfectly harmless. And yet it would not be wisdom to engage in controversy over this subject" (letter 17a, 1893, quoted in 2SM 279).

In her response she makes five points. Let us consider them in the order in her letter.

1. "Your questions, I will say, are answered largely, if not definitely, in *How to Live.*" The reader will note that Ellen White refers Caro and his fellow students back to *How to Live,* in which she feels she has already answered his question. In her article on drug medication in *How to Live* she saw several sick individuals. In each case a physician administered one or more "drug poisons." The drugs named are opium (contains morphine and codeine), calomel (a mercury compound), and nux vomica (strychnine). Next she observes the results of such treatment, and reveals, in some detail, its effect. The patients all die. Finally the "Great Physician" relates how proper physiological procedures might have saved both suffering and lives. Clearly the three medicines she refers to represent the type of agent she called "drugs."

Then she reinforces her answer by accepting Caro's grouping of remedies: "Drug poisons mean the articles which you have mentioned." The medical student had called them "stronger medicines" or "drugs." Ellen White referred to them as "drug poisons." She clearly agreed with Caro as to what he and others called "drugs." The medical student cited three examples of the type of medicinal agent to which he was referring, namely, mercury, strychnine, and arsenic. Ellen White had seen in vision opium, strychnine, and calomel. Between the two statements made by Caro and Ellen White we have four examples of what they both meant by drugs: opium, strychnine, arsenic, and mercury. Thus when she used "drug" she had in mind strong, harsh, and poisonous medicines.

The third point to consider, which I believe is a final clarification of what Ellen White had in mind by "drug," appears in Caro's inquiry. Note his question: "Does it refer only to the stronger medicines . . . or does it also include the simpler remedies?" She answers, "Drug poisons mean the articles which you have mentioned." Her reply excludes the simpler, less harmful remedies.

2. She then responds to his second question regarding "simpler remedies": "The simpler remedies are less harmful in proportion to their simplicity." Again she accepts Caro's grouping of medicines but points out that the simpler or simple remedies are themselves not harmless and should be used with caution. It would have been helpful if Caro, rather than ending his short list of examples with an "etc.," had named additional agents. But since he did not, we must work with the information at hand. Both potassium and iodine are inorganic elements needed by the body. Current medical practice employs both in appropriate doses for patients receiving certain diuretics and for preventing or treating simple goiter.

The third example mentioned is the "squills." At the time Caro wrote, physicians prescribed squill as a syrup, tincture, or fluid extract and used it as an expectorant, cardiac stimulant, and diuretic. Webster describes squill as follows:

"The cut and dried fleshy inner scales of the bulb of the white variety of *Urgenia scilla,* or the younger bulbs of *U. indica.* . . . It contains one or more physiologically active glucosides and is used as an expectorant, cardiac stimulant, and diuretic."[14]

The uses of squill have not changed since Caro's time, but pharmacology has more carefully established the relevant components. In time similar glucosides found in the foxglove replaced those obtained from squill. The preparations from the foxglove were less toxic. Medical science long ago isolated and purified the active glucosides and has used them for decades without concern as to source.

I would like to share an experience I had while I was an intern at the White Memorial Hospital, in Los Angeles. A patient had severe heart failure and was receiving digitalis (foxglove), first in powder form and then as an extract. The purified glucosides were not available at that time. The digitalis ravaged him with vomiting, diarrhea, and severe cramps. As he sat on the side of his bed, he looked at me and said, "Doctor, I would rather die than take this stuff any longer."

Today digoxin (lanoxin), a purified glucoside, prescribed as a drug, is the most commonly used agent for certain forms of heart failure. The toxic responses are negligible, if any, providing the attending medical staff keep the blood levels in the normal range.

3. "There are simple herbs and roots that every family may use for themselves." We will discuss simple herbs and roots at length in chapter 8.

4. "I do not think that I can give you any definite line of medicines compounded and dealt out by doctors, that are perfectly harmless" (*ibid.*). What medicines was Ellen White referring to? Since she definitely opposed the use of strong medicines and poisonous drugs she must be speaking of the simpler remedies and the simple herbs and roots. The following 1902 statement, I believe, will clarify the matter:

"The common words by which we know simple remedies[15] are as useful as are the technical terms used by physicians for these same remedies. To request a nurse to prepare some catnip tea, answers the purpose fully as well as would directions given her in language understood only after long study" (manuscript 169, 1902, quoted in 19MR 48).

It is evident that Ellen White was recommending remedies employed by the medical profession, and that physicians used Latin when prescribing them.[16] While not condemning this group of medicines she was, however, unable to draw a line between those that are less harmful (digoxin, caffeine, aspirin) and those that are virtually harmless (hop and catnip tea, red clover tea). How does one arbitrarily set such boundaries? Medicinal herbs are not harmless, and all drugs do not carry the same level of toxicity. Ellen White was wise in not committing herself to some form of classification. The size of dose and the manner of administration can transform a harmless substance into a toxic agent. To lump medicines into the kind of categories under discussion would be arbitrary at best. Ellen White could not do it. Nor can the author.

From this and other statements we can conclude that she used the word "drug" to refer to the "stronger medicines" or "drug poisons," and was not including the "simpler remedies" she advocated and that were also used by physicians. Examples of the latter class of agents, which she herself employed, would be catnip tea, hop tea, strong coffee, and dark tea, the latter two consumed only as medicine (letter 12, 1888, quoted in CD 490; manuscript 3, 1888, quoted in 2SM 301, 302; letter 20, 1882, quoted in 2SM 302, 303).

Caffeine is the active ingredient of both tea and coffee and would be considered among the "simpler remedies" that are "less harmful" in contrast to the "drug poisons" referred to earlier. Notice what she said regarding her using tea and coffee only as medicine: "I do not preach one thing and practice another. I do not present to my hearers rules of life for them to follow while I make an exception in my own case" (2SM 302).

She then tells Caro:

5. "And yet it would not be wisdom to engage in controversy over this subject" (2SM 279). Unfortunately, through the years and to the present time a continuing conflict has existed and still continues between those who conservatively use medications and those who hold that all "drugs" prescribed by physicians are off limits and restrict themselves to the use of medicinal herbs, hydrotherapy, and other natural remedies. Ellen White's comment is indeed inspired

counsel. If specialists in the field of medicine find it impossible to place the different kinds of agents used for the "cure, mitigation, or prevention of disease" in neat compartments, why should we who are awaiting the coming of our Lord quarrel over the subject?

Medicines Ellen White Considered as Drugs

Strong, harsh, poisonous drugs and concoctions received Ellen White's scathing rebuke. In 1896 she declared, "I tell you this because I dare not withhold it. Christ paid too much for man's redemption to have his body so ruthlessly treated by drug medication" (letter 73, 1896, MM 229).

A year later she added, "Drug medication is to be discarded. On this point the conscience of the physician must ever be kept tender and true and clean. The inclination to use poisonous drugs, which kill if they do not cure, needs to be guarded against" (manuscript 162, 1897, *ibid.* 227).

"The treatment we gave when the sanitarium was first established required earnest labor to combat disease. We did not use drug concoctions; we followed hygienic methods. The work was blessed by God. . . . To carry out the light on this subject, to practice hygienic treatment, and to educate on altogether different lines of treating the sick, was the reason given me why we should have sanitariums established in various localities" (letter 82, 1897, 2SM 293).

"Right and correct habits, intelligently and perseveringly practiced, will be removing the cause for disease, and the strong drugs need not be resorted to" (manuscript 22, 1887, MM 222).

"Our people should become intelligent in the treatment of sickness without the aid of poisonous drugs" (manuscript 162, 1897, *ibid.* 227). "Powerful poisons are often administered, which fetter nature in all her friendly efforts to recover from the abuse the system has suffered" (*How to Live,* No. 3, 1865, 2SM 441). "Every poisonous preparation in the vegetable and mineral kingdoms, taken into the system, will leave its wretched influence, affecting the liver and lungs, and deranging the system generally" (4SG 140, 1864, *ibid.* 281).

Summary

When Ellen White condemned "drugs," she employed the word to refer to a specific class of agents: powerful poisons, poisonous drugs, strong drugs, and drug concoctions. She did not include as this type of drugs such things as teas derived from catnip, hops, regular tea, and coffee or the many other agents dispensed by physicians.

While clarifying which drugs they should or should not use, she at the same time encouraged all to adopt healthful lifestyles that, in most cases, would remove the cause of the disease, not just alter the symptoms.

References

[1] Leslie Z. Benet, in Louis S. Goodman and Alfred G. Gilman, *The Pharmacological Basis of Therapeutics,* 9th ed. (New York: McGraw-Hill, 1995), p. 1.

[2] Howard C. Kutchai, "Membrane Receptors, Second Messengers, and Signal Transduction Pathways," in *Physiology,* eds. Robert M. Berne and Matthew N. Levy, 3rd ed. (Boston: Mosby Year Book, 1993), p. 77.

[3] Elliott M. Ross, "Mechanisms of Drug Action and the Relationship Between Drug Concentration and Effect," in Goodman and Gilman, p. 29.

[4] *Webster's New International Dictionary of the English Language,* 2nd ed. (G. & C. Merriam Company, Inc., 1949).

[5] Adolph M. Hutter, Jr., "Congestive Heart Failure," in *Scientific American Medicine,* eds. David C. Dale and Daniel D. Federman (New York: Scientific American, 1996).

[6] Gerald L. Mandell and William A. Petri, Jr., "Penicillins, Cephalosporins, and Other B-Lactam Antibiotics," in Goodman and Gilman, pp. 1074-1076.

[7] Ross, p. 37.

[8] Mary J. Mycek, Richard A. Harvey, and Pamela C. Champe, *Lippincott's Illustrated Reviews: Pharmacology,* 2nd ed. (Philadelphia: Lippincott-Raven Publishers, 1997), pp. 1-16.

[9] Kenneth S. Babe, Jr., and William E. Serafin, "Histamine, Bradykinin, and Their Antagonists," in Goodman and Gilman, pp. 581-586.

[10] Roger V. Stambaugh, Albert F. Morgan, and Cyral O. Enwonwu, "Ascorbic Acid Deficiency Associated With Dilantin Hyperplasia," *Journal of Periodontology* 44, No. 4: 244-247.

[11] Mandell and Petri, pp. 1086-1089.

[12] Interestingly, Dr. David Paulson was, at that time, a classmate of Caro's.

[13] *Merriam-Webster's Collegiate Dictionary,* 10th ed. (Springfield, Mass.: Merriam-Webster, 1998).

[14] *Webster's New International Dictionary of the English Language,* 2nd ed., unabridged (Springfield, Mass.: G. & C. Merriam Co., 1957).

[15] Chapter 9 will examine simple remedies in detail.

[16] In 1897 she commented, "I would not touch their nostrums, to which they give Latin names. I am determined to know, in straight English, the name of everything that I introduce into my system" (2SM 290).

CHAPTER FIVE

A Physician Explains . . .

DRUGS DENOUNCED BY REFORMERS

SECTION I

A Reformation Starts

The medical revolution in medicine did not blossom all at once, nor was it a smooth transition from old to new. It was a jagged uphill climb from the darkness of the valleys of traditional practice to the growing light atop the summit. Each change elicited suspicion and took time to be accepted, if accepted at all. Some of the leading reformers were physicians who, seeing the terrible results from the medicine they and their colleagues were using, realized that there must be something better but hardly knew which direction to take.

As the years went by, medical education improved. Physiology, chemistry, pharmacology, microbiology, and others became a required part of the training of physicians. Such exposure to science introduced into the field of medicine a new breed of physicians willing to question traditional methods of diagnosing and treating disease. While many medical outlooks and traditional procedures were changed reluctantly, change they did nevertheless. But not all the reformers were physicians. A few were like Sylvester Graham, a preacher, and Mary Baker Eddy, a housewife. And then Ellen White joined the reform movement.

Rural and Urban America (Early and Mid-Nineteenth Century)

Disease in America was rampant and the practice of medicine

rather primitive. Life expectancy hovered around 40 years. Early settlers often suffered from malnutrition, making them more susceptible to infectious diseases. The diseases most feared were malaria and dysentery in the summer, and influenza and pneumonia in the winter. In addition, periodic outbreaks of smallpox, yellow fever, cholera, and diphtheria would sweep through the nation. People constantly feared typhoid fever, typhus, scarlet fever, measles, whooping cough, and—above all—tuberculosis (sometimes called consumption or phthisis), the greatest killer of all.

As living conditions improved, so did the health of Americans. However, as cities enlarged in size with the Industrial Revolution, their environment deteriorated. Lemuel Shattuck of Massachusetts sadly reported in 1850 that "London, with its imperfect supply of water—its narrow, crowded streets—its foul cesspools—its hopeless pauperism—its crowded graveyards—and its other monstrous sanitary evils, is as healthy a city as Boston,"[1] and "in some respects more so."[2]

How Early Medicine Treated Diseases

The historians Albert Lyons and Joseph Petrucelli succinctly describe the practice of medicine during this period: "In the early years of the nineteenth century, the principal therapies open to European and American physicians were general regimens of diet, exercise, rest, baths and massage, bloodletting, scarification, cupping, blistering, sweating, emetics, purges, enemas, and fumigations. There were multitudes of plant and mineral drugs available, but only a few rested on sound physiological or even empiric foundations: quinine for malaria, digitalis for heart failure, colchicine for gout, and opiates for pain. Many physicians continued to use compounds of arsenic for such diverse complaints as intermittent fever, paralysis, epilepsy, edema, rickets, heart disease, cancer, skin ulcerations, parasites, indigestion, and general debility. Antimony, which had its heyday in the previous century, was also still much in use, possibly sometimes aiding patients with parasitic infestations. For the most part, leading European practitioners, as well as some in America, permitted illnesses to run their course without interference, for careful observers noted little benefit from the therapies available. On the other hand, others believed that 'desperate diseases require desperate measures' and favored the use of drastic drugs and procedures."[3]

While the discovery of germs encouraged the identification of diseases, it was slow to do anything for their prevention and cure. It did, in subtle ways, begin to change the focus of therapy, though. However, in the United States, especially in frontier medicine, physicians at large hesitated to discard traditional remedies, since they had little to replace them with.[4] While a small number of physicians used supportive measures in treating their patients, the majority followed the teachings of Rush and his admiring practitioners who believed that nature "should be driven from the sick room as should a stray dog or cat."[5] Besides employing the heroic measures of bloodletting, blistering, scarification, and cupping, they prescribed large numbers of drugs in high dosage. They believed that "desperate diseases require desperate measures."[6] One contemporary physician recalled that "when dispensing medicine to a patient, it was quite common for him to say, 'Now, Doctor, if you give me a dose, give me a big one.'"[7] Physicians were happy to comply in order to curry favor with their patients.

For the reader to get a clearer picture of what "these measures" meant, the author suggests that the reader reread chapters 2 and 3. However, a brief statement will refresh the memory. Definitions of the following terms come from Webster's dictionary.[8]

Drastic: "Acting rapidly and violently; opposed to *bland;* as, *drastic* purgatives." Drastic purgatives included such herbal preparations as podophyllum, colocynth, jalap, and croton oil. Croton oil will produce blisters when applied to the skin. Such substances caused severe cramping, and the stool was often a bloody discharge. The "drastics" were a class of agents that produced the most severe responses for whatever they were prescribed, such as vomiting and sweating.

Blistering: "Raising, or severe enough to raise, blisters; scorching." Materials commonly used to accomplish blistering included mustard plasters, preparations containing cantharides (from the blister beetle or Spanish fly); and croton oil. They actually produced chemical burns when applied to the skin over the area believed to be involved in the illness. For example, physicians might prescribe them for the chest in the case of pleurisy, the abdomen in typhus fever, the joints for rheumatism, and the neck and the throat for laryngitis. The fluid of the blister, when drained away, supposedly removed the disease-causing substance. The blisters frequently became infected, and besides torturing the patient, eventually contributed to their death.

Cupping: "The operation of drawing blood to or from the surface of the body by forming a partial vacuum over a certain spot. It is called *wet cupping,* when the skin is scratched; otherwise *dry cupping.*" When every means possible to remove blood and fluids from the patient was believed necessary, cupping was not an uncommon practice. The instrument used for "wet cupping" was a scarificator. *Scarificator:* An instrument for making slight cuts in the skin, esp. one containing several lancets moved by a spring."

Since medical science as yet had no local or general anesthetics to ease the pain, the suffering caused by such practices was torture! Sometimes the physician gave opium to dull the senses. Frequently the patient endured numerous procedures at the same time. We should remember that the patient was already sick. Such treatments surely hastened the death of countless victims.

Reforms Take Place Gradually

But gradually, at first almost imperceptibly, voices of dissent, sometimes soft, sometimes strident, began to make themselves heard. Here and there advocates, medical and lay people alike, arose to claim that nature possessed healing powers. That harsh remedies aggravated disease while nature, if aided by the most simple medicines, could accomplish wonders. They pleaded for physicians to allow the natural forces or systems of the body a chance to heal the patient.

Support for such views came from the rising death rate seen among patients treated by orthodox medicine.[9] The medical historian Richard Shryock, looking at the problems of drug medications, observed that there was "more skepticism about the value of drugs during the later nineteenth century than in any other period."[10]

Reformers Attack Drugging

The reformers opposed the harsh or heroic measures used in treating the sick. Drugging and bleeding especially became points of attack.

Dr. J. Marion Sims, soon after his graduation from medical school in 1835, expressed himself strongly about the deplorable treatment of the sick. "The practice at that time was heroic: it was murderous. I know nothing about medicine, but I had sense enough to see that doctors were killing their patients, that medicine was not an exact science, that it was wholly empirical and that it would be better to trust entirely to nature than to the hazardous skill of the doctors."[11]

Mercury Attacked

One of the most widely prescribed of all agents was the mercurial compound calomel. William Rothstein, a medical historian, in his book *American Physicians in the Nineteenth Century* quotes a physician regarding its use: "'When a practitioner was puzzled about the administration of any medicine in a disease, it was deemed perfectly proper for him to prescribe a dose of calomel; which he did conscientiously, with well satisfied assurance, that if he did not give the exact medicine adapted to the case, he could not be far wrong!' Many physicians believed that the omission of calomel in desperate cases was tantamount to abandoning the patient without a final saving effort."[12]

Unfortunately, calomel was given to many patients for long periods of time. The drug is cumulative, that is, it is retained in the body, so the amount present in the body gradually increases even when the daily dose is small. The early symptoms are purging, and salivation. Then the gums, tongue, and salivary glands become inflamed and painful. Finally "the mouth feels unusually hot, and is sometimes sensible of a coppery or metallic taste; the gums are swollen, red, and tender; ulcers make their appearance and spread in all directions; the saliva is thick and stringy, and has that peculiar, offensive odor characteristic of mercurial disease; the tongue is swollen and stiff, and there is some fever, with derangement of the secretions. The disease progressing, it destroys every part that it touches, until the lips, the cheeks, and even the bones have been eaten away before death comes to the sufferer's relief."[13]

Because of their ignorance of human physiology, traditional physicians had to limit their procedures and remedies to those currently available. And that led to a dismal and deadly routine. But as the number of more scientifically trained graduates increased, hostility to such severe practices intensified. Here is the advice of a physician to his colleagues during this period.

"It is but the other day that I saw a case of gastroenteritis, in which calomel was pushed till the countenance exhibited a most frightful appearance, owing to the excessive swelling of the cheeks, lips, tongue, fauces, and throat, while the saliva flowed in streams.

"It is this observation of this injudicious use of mercury, by the common people, at the instigation of interested quacks, and unprincipled men in our own profession, that has caused such a hue and cry, . . . which has produced a war for its utter and entire destruction and annihilation, that rages in many parts of our country with as much venom, fury, and heat, as ever did feudal war or party politics. . . . Under these circumstances, is it not better to conciliate the prejudice of the people, and inspire their confidence and support, by dispensing with its 'use and substituting in its stead vegetable articles.' "[14]

"The effects of the treatments of early nineteenth-century physicians on the patient are difficult for the modern mind to contemplate."[15]

Reform Movements

The reformers did not arise all at once. But each attempted to find some form of treatment other than that available through traditional medicine.

Homeopathy

Perhaps the most influential and widely accepted of the reform movements was that of homeopathy, initiated in the 1790s by Samuel Hahnemann (1755-1843) of Leipzig, Germany. Large numbers of disillusioned physicians in Europe and America, and much of the lay population as well, adopted his teachings, and they held sway for some 100 years. Not only did he object to bloodletting, blistering, catharsis, and other commonly used procedures, he also opposed the powerful and haphazardly compounded drugs in use. Instead he advocated proper diet, fresh air, and exercise as methods of treatment, and encouraged personal and domestic hygiene.

Hahnemann taught that a drug causing nausea, vomiting, diarrhea, or fever in a healthy individual would cure a sick person with similar symptoms. He called his "law" that "like is cured by like" homeopathy. Also he believed that large doses of a drug disguised its true effects. As a result he recommended extremely small—even infinitesimal—doses.[16]

As expected, the regular medical community, whom he called allopathic practitioners (allopaths or MDs), ridiculed Hahnemann. Despite that, patients recovered when treated homeopathically. The minute doses of the standard medications did no harm nor did they do what Hahnemann believed they did, but did provide time for the natural recuperative powers of the body to work. They also gave the patient the belief they were taking something beneficial (the placebo effect). In addition, his promotion of a wholesome diet, fresh air, and exercise did much good, giving support to those who believed in the healing powers of nature. Those who followed him remained unaware of the placebo effect. It is significant that he prescribed most of the common drugs used by physicians, but in minute doses. The following examples illustrate the point: Nux-vomica (strychnine), sulphur, lobelia (nicotine), phosphorus, ipecac, hydrochloric acid, alcohol (a remedy and slightly nutritious substance), plumbum (lead), arsenic, colchicine, jalap, senna, mercury, aconite, belladonna (atropine), podophyllum, camphor, veratrum, staphysagria, opium, quinine, cantharides, croton, phosphoric acid, tartar emetic, iodine, and numerous other agents.[17]

Opposition to Regular Physicians

As mentioned earlier, of all the reform movements homeopathy was the strongest challenge to regular medicine. The issue involved not the drugs themselves but the massive doses prescribed. Note what the authors of *The Homeopathic Practice of Medicine*, published in 1864, have to say:

"The chief remedies of the old school are the preparations of mercury, opium, antimony, and bark. . . . Indeed scarcely a single malady of any moment can be named, in which one of these medicines is not considered indispensable."[18] The authors then single out each agent and present its dangers.

Mercury

"This is the substance with which unfortunate mortals are drugged, from the time they come into the world until their wretched and too often premature departure, with its well-known and generally admitted evils and dangers."[19]

Opium

"Possessing the power, as it does in an imminent degree, when exhibited in large doses, of covering (not curing) symptoms, and of *shutting* the mouths of clamorous and inquiring patients, it is used constantly and indiscriminately in nearly all protracted maladies."[20]

Antimony (Tartar Emetic) has its own problems:

"When it fails to produce emesis (vomiting) speedily, it often acts violently upon the bowels, giving rise to severe griping pains and watery evacuations. The tenderness of the stomach and intestines, and the constitutional disturbance which succeeds its emetic and cathartic operation, indicates the injury which these delicate structures have sustained."[21]

Cinchona

"Quinine is the remedy upon which universal reliance is placed; possessing the property, when used in large and repeated doses, of speedily arresting the chills and fever, it is constantly prescribed for this malady [malaria], without the slightest knowledge of its specific powers, and without any regard to the dangerous medicinal disorders, which it superinduces."[22] The authors continue to recite other problems from the wide use of quinine, ending their discussion with the statement: "These monstrous quantities create (say Wood and Bache) 'gastroenteritic irritation, nausea, griping, purging, headache, giddiness, fever, somnolency, in some cases delirium, in others stupor, etc.'"[23]

Their indictment of drugs continues, but rather than discussing agent by agent, the authors criticize classes of drugs. "There are many other medicines employed by allopathy [regular physicians] in the treatment of disease, besides those to which we have alluded, but in general they serve only as *auxilaries*. In this list may be ranked diaphoretics [induce sweating], diuretics, expectorants [eject matter from throat and lungs], refrigerants [reduce body heat], emmenagogues [promote menstrual discharge], emollients [soothe skin and mucous membranes], errhines [provoke sneezing], etc., but the articles belonging to each of these classes, in a crude state and in large doses are liable to important objections."[24]

In time homeopathic physicians began using larger doses, reasoning that "a certain margin is left within which specifics [drugs] given in more massive doses may still have curative effects."[25] Dr. I. D. Johnson, in his *Guide to Homeopathic Practice* (1913), is more outspoken: "Every physician, therefore, should use his own judgment, and prescribe such doses as will most quickly and safely cure his patient; and if facts prove, as all homeopaths believe, that the attenuated doses are the most efficient when administered upon the homeopathic law, then it is the duty of all to give these preparations the preference."[26] While allowing for larger doses, he still urges for smaller ones.

Thompsonian Reforms

The practice of botanical medicine, based on roots and herbs, was quite well known, widely accepted, and considered highly beneficial. But such "natural doctors" had limited formal training and were hostile to regular medical practice. Samuel Thompson

(1769-1843) championed such a system in his book *New Guide to Health: or, Botanic Family Physician,* in which he stressed nature's remedies and folk medicine.

An eloquent speaker and a capable writer, Thompson used his pen and voice to attack mercury, opium, arsenic, nitre, and the lancet. Bleeding, he taught, was unnatural, injurious, and absurd, and doctors should abandon the procedure. Blistering was inhumane and dangerous. The regular medicines were poisonous and lethal. Many intelligent physicians supported his views and used, instead of strong drugs and compound mixtures, "simples," or medicines composed of a single botanic drug, which, they believed, would aid nature's processes. The benefits of his approach derived not from the agents he used but rather from the agents and procedures he did not use.[27]

Thompson, like other physicians of his day, believed that most illnesses resulted from problems arising in the stomach and liver. Hence his medical approach was an attempt to cleanse and strengthen these organs and improve their functions.

Eclectics

The eclectics were a reform group of physicians who attempted to be more selective in the medications and procedures they used, a practice that earned them their name. They used less drastic measures in treatment and attempted to emphasize herbal medicines, discarding bloodletting and medicines such as arsenic and mercury. Also they attempted to diagnose a patient's needs more carefully and to treat more specifically what they observed. The growing scientific knowledge in the basic sciences of medicine gradually faded the interest in eclectic medicine.[28]

Osteopathy

Andrew Still (1828-1917) began osteopathy in the latter part of the nineteenth century. Along with the reformers before him, he opposed drug therapy and initiated the system called osteopathy. He believed that a proper alignment of the bones would restore the body's functions to normal. In time, however, while still emphasizing the relationship of body structure to function, standard medical methods of treatment, which the system had never wholly discarded, came back into use. Osteopathy became almost identical to regular medicine.[29]

Chiropractic

Another system of healing that denounced drugs held that the malalignment of the bones of the vertebral column (back) caused illness and disease. Daniel D. Palmer (1845-1913) in 1895 founded chiropractic, claiming that appropriate adjustments of the spinal column would cure ailments of the internal organs. Chiropractic recommends a wholesome diet, exercise, and other health-promoting activities.[30]

Christian Science

A housewife named Mary Baker Eddy (1821-1910) launched a philosophy of mind-body connections that emphasized the relationship between prayer and healing. In 1875 she published *Science and Health With Key to the Scriptures,* which outlines the principles she promoted, and four years later she established the Church of Christ, Scientist. Its members revere her book alongside the Bible. The system it taught is known as Christian Science, and its followers call themselves Christian Scientists. Their official spiritual leaders go by the name of Christian Science practitioners. The key principle of Christian Science teaching relies on prayer and spiritual awakening, not on medications and other measures used by physicians. Faithful followers have, at times, refused treatment for their children who had diseases curable by conventional therapy. Lawsuits have arisen over such incidents.[31]

Drug/Health Reform Movements

Besides opposing the orthodox system of medicine with its harsh treatments and reliance on powerful drugs, a number of health reformers advocated, to varying extents, changes in lifestyle that would promote wellness and prevent disease.

Sylvester Graham, a minister turned reformer, developed one

of the most popular health movements during the 1830s. Not only did he reject most potent medications, but he stressed exercise, the free use of water both internally and externally, and temperance in eating and drinking. Perhaps he was most noted for his advocacy of "Graham" or unrefined bread to which his name still clings. Attempting to place his teachings on a scientific basis, he included current physiology as well as hygiene in his instructions.

The Graham movement later merged with hydropathy, advocating water cures. The chief genius of such establishments was Dr. Russell T. Trall, who expanded his program to include a health institute and hydrotherapeutic college. Dr. James C. Jackson, another reform-minded physician, established a health institute in Dansville, New York. Lorenzo and Orson Fowler, who actively spread the social gospel of phrenology, joined with Trall, the Grahamites, and others to champion therapeutic, dress, and health reforms.[32]

Summary

The drug reform movements—homeopathy, Thompsonians, eclectics, osteopathy, chiropractic, and Christian Scientists, plus disillusioned regular physicians and a large segment of the laity—dealt a telling blow against the system of drugging. To their impact we should add that of the drug/health reformers. By the beginning of the twentieth century both the type and use of drugs had changed. But unfortunately the focus of treating the sick had not altered and still emphasized drug therapy.

Shryock, in his history of modern medical practice, concludes that "the real debt of modern hygiene to these health reformers is seldom appreciated; the very principles for which Graham, Trall, and others fought—the danger of drugs, the importance of hygiene, and the ounce-of-prevention philosophy in general—were in due time largely accepted by the regular profession."[33]

SECTION II

Ellen White, a Reformer With a Vision
In 1863 Ellen White received from the Lord counsels regarding

health reform. They made her aware of the harmful effects of the poisonous drugs prescribed by physicians at the time, which, more often than not, did more harm than good. She herself had a bitter experience in the loss of her eldest son a few months after she received her first vision on health reform. Dores Robinson relates the experience of the White family: "The family physician, who was called in, *took measures that only hastened the fatal outcome,* and a few days later the saddened family were returning to Battle Creek, where they laid Henry to rest in the Oak Hill Cemetery."[34] Ellen White uses strong words to condemn the medical drugging business.

Strong Drugs Are Killers

Compelled to oppose the harsh and heroic drugging so prevalent, she wrote in 1864: "I was shown that more deaths have been caused by drug-taking than from all other causes combined. . . . Multitudes of physicians, and multitudes of drugs, have cursed the inhabitants of the earth, and have carried thousands and tens of thousands to untimely graves" (4SG 133). Almost 40 years later she wrote: "A practice that is laying the foundation of a vast amount of disease and of even more serious evils, is the free use of poisonous drugs" ([1905] MH 126).

Three of these commonly used poisonous agents especially concerned her: "Mercury, calomel, and quinine have brought their amount of wretchedness, which the day of God alone will fully reveal. Preparations of mercury and calomel taken into the system *ever retain their poisonous strength as long as there is a particle of it left in the system.* These poisonous preparations have destroyed their millions, and left sufferers upon the earth to linger out a miserable existence. All are better off without these dangerous mixtures. Miserable sufferers, with disease in almost every form, misshapen by suffering, with dreadful ulcers, and pains in the bones, loss of teeth, loss of memory, and impaired sight, are to be seen almost everywhere. They are victims of poisonous preparations" (4aSG 139 [1864]; italics supplied).

Years later she had not lost her burden to expose the nature of these medications. "I tell you this because I dare not withhold it," she penned in 1896. "Christ paid too much for man's redemption to have his body so ruthlessly treated as it has been by drug medication" (letter 73, 1896, quoted in MM 229). "Drug medication is to be discarded," she wrote the next year (manuscript 162, 1897, *ibid.* 227).

Mixtures and Concoctions

Ellen White contrasted the simple remedies with another group of agents called compounds or mixtures. They could be combinations of various substances. Ellen White refers to such combinations of drugs as both mixtures and concoctions. Here are a few examples:

"The endless variety of medicines in the market, the numerous advertisements of new drugs and mixtures, all of which, as they say, do wonderful cures, kill hundreds where they benefit one. Those who are sick are not patient. They will take the various medicines, some of which are very powerful, although they know nothing of the nature of the mixtures. All the medicines they take only make their recovery more hopeless. Yet they keep dosing, and continue to grow weaker, until they die. Some will have medicine at all events. Then let them take these hurtful mixtures and the various deadly poisons upon their own responsibility. God's servants should not administer medicines which they know will leave behind injurious effects upon the system, even if they do relieve present suffering" (4aSG 139, 140 [1864]).

"The practitioners are very much in earnest in using their dangerous concoctions, and I am decidedly opposed to resorting to such things" (letter 170, 1893, 2SM 279).

"The treatment we gave when the sanitarium was first established required earnest labor to combat disease. We did not use drug concoctions; we followed hygienic methods. This work was blessed by God" (letter 82, 1897, *ibid.* 293).

The Long-term Effects of Drugs

Exposure to chemicals, whether they be regular or botanic drugs, can lead to different types of toxic reactions. As we have pointed out earlier, drugs may have acute or chronic effects. Acute effects appear immediately after use. Chronic, as you would expect, develop some time later. Some toxic effects may not show until weeks, months, or even years later (delayed toxicity).

The effects of any drug should be reversible unless they are highly toxic. If a drug injures some tissue, say the liver, that can produce new cells quite readily, the effect of the drug is reversible. If it involves the central nervous system, the tissue damage is probably permanent, since neurons rarely regenerate themselves. An example of a delayed toxic effect is an antibiotic (chloramphenicol) that blocks the bone marrow from producing blood cells, causing aplastic anemia weeks afterward. Many cancer-producing (carcinogenic) agents may lie dormant for 20, 30, or more years before triggering tumors.[35]

Today physicians no longer prescribe lead, mercury, arsenic, and cadmium as medicines. However, a contaminated environment may expose human beings to such dangerous substances. The solder of water pipes may contain lead, and mercury may be present in fish eaten as food, or from the amalgam in tooth fillings. Arsenic naturally contaminates drinking water in various parts of the world. Tobacco smoke contains cadmium (a one-pack-a-day smoker retains about 1 milligram cadmium per year), and it may also enter foods grown on contaminated soils.[36]

In the next several statements Ellen White repeatedly points out that regardless of their immediate effects, some drugs have residual actions that may be long delayed. They may "produce for the time being favorable results, but will implant in the system that which will cause great difficulties hereafter, which they many never recover from during their lifetime" (manuscript 22, 1887, quoted in MM 224, 225). "[The physician who depends on drug medication] is introducing into the system a seed crop that will never lose its destroying properties throughout the lifetime" (letter 73, 1896, quoted in MM 229, 2SM 284). She further adds that drugs, along with alcohol, tea, and coffee, always leave traces of evil behind them" (manuscript 162, 1897, MM 228).

Then she contrasts the effects of the simple remedies with

those of the drug poisons, and suggests that the latter may hinder the actions of the less powerful agents. "But the simplest remedies may assist nature, and leave no baleful effects after their use" (letter 82, 1897, 2SM 294). "Others [sanitarium patients] have carried the drugs away with them, making less effective the simple remedies nature uses to restore the system" (letter 67, 1899, 3MR 305). "Nature's simple remedies will aid in recovery without leaving the deadly aftereffects so often felt by those who use poisonous drugs" (letter 82, 1908, 2SM 281).

When she speaks above of the effects of long-term exposure to poisonous drugs, she was doubtless thinking of mercury poisoning. "Preparations of mercury and calomel taken into the system ever retain their poisonous strength as long as there is a particle of it left in the system. . . . Miserable sufferers, with disease in almost every form, misshapen by suffering, with dreadful ulcers, and pains in the bones, loss of teeth, loss of memory, and impaired sight, are to be seen almost every where. They are victims of poisonous preparations" (4aSG 139 [1864]). Calomel (chloride of mercury) was probably the most widely used agent. It was used in both small and large doses and over considerable periods of time. Because of its cumulative effect, chronic mercury poisoning was not uncommon. Beginning with pain and swelling of the structures of the mouth and salivary glands, the teeth would loosen and fall out, and ulcers would form and spread destroying the tissues of the lips, cheeks, palate, and mandibles. Her description fits extremely well.

The use of the bark that served as the source of quinine was widespread. Although it was effective only against certain forms of malaria, many often gave it for fevers in general. It was also a popular drug for a variety of illnesses. Interestingly, Ellen White condemned its general use. Note the following: "Knowledge is what is needed. Drugs are too often promised to restore health, and the poor sick are so thoroughly drugged with quinine, morphine, or some strong health- and life-destroying medicine, that nature may never make sufficient protest, but give up the struggle, and they may continue their wrong habits with hopeful immunity" (manuscript 22, 1887, 15MR 276).

However, while she lived in Australia, a former missionary among the South Pacific islands asked her if he had done wrong in withholding quinine from his firstborn son, who had had a serious case of malaria. He had read her counsels in the *Testimonies* and had refused to administer the drug. As a result his son had died. When he met Ellen White, he inquired, "'Would I have sinned to give the boy quinine when I knew of no other way to check malaria and when the prospect was that he would die without it?' In reply she said, 'No, we are expected to do the best we can'" (W. C. White letter, Sept. 10, 1935, in 2SM 281, 282, footnote).

My brother Leslie and I had more than one experience with quinine. The last time I remember taking it was when both my brother and I came down with malaria. Quinine was the only known antimalarial drug at the time. We received massive doses for an extended period. As I look back at the experience, neither the size of dose nor the length of time we took the medicine was necessary. One of the long-term effects of toxic amounts of quinine is permanent damage to the eighth cranial nerves, the auditory nerves. Both of us still have ringing in our ears (tinnitus) 76 years later!

Drugs Attacked for General Reasons

Ellen White questioned drugs for a number of reasons. She said that the actions of drugs are not compatible with the functioning of the body. "The use of drugs is not favorable or natural to the laws of life and health. The drug medication gives nature two burdens to bear, in the place of one. She has two serious difficulties to overcome, in the place of one" (*Health, Or, How to Live*, No. 3, 1865, p. 57, quoted in MM 223). Today we understand the task placed on the liver and kidneys in breaking down and excreting certain medications. "Drug medication . . . lays a foundation in the human organism for a twofold greater evil than that which they claim to have relieved" (manuscript 22, 1887, *ibid.* 222).

Here she makes a number of nonspecific criticisms on drugs: "The practitioners are very much in earnest in using their dangerous concoctions, and I am decidedly opposed to resorting to such things. They never cure; they may change the difficulty to create a worse one" (letter 17a, 1893, 2SM 279).

Although condemning the actions of drugs she encourages agents and procedures that will support the body's natural recuperative powers. "Use nature's remedies—water, sunshine, and fresh air. Do not use drugs. Drugs never heal; they only change the features of the disease" (letter 116, 1903, PC 17). "They [the poisonous drugs] destroy the power of the patient to help himself" (letter 82, 1908, 2SM 281).

Drugs Attacked for Specific Reasons

The various medical reformers attacked the strong poisonous drugs in common use because of the effects they observed in those receiving them. Ellen White, also on occasion, described the effects of such medicines. It is of some interest to see that she generally points out the harm they do to the body's organs and systems.

"Medicine deranges nature's fine machinery, and breaks down the constitution and kills, but never cures" (*How to Live*, No. 3, 1865, 2SM 448). "Drugs always have a tendency to break down and destroy vital forces" (manuscript 22, 1887, *ibid.* 281). "Drugs, in the place of helping nature, are constantly paralyzing her efforts" (MM 224). "Drug medication has broken up the power of the human machinery, and the patients have died" (letter 67, 1899, 3MR 305). "We discourage the use of drugs, for they poison the current of the blood" (manuscript 49, 1908, CD 303).

Unworthy Reasons for Using Drugs

She also opposed the use of drugs because of impatience, hard work, laziness, or unwillingness to face the real cause of the illness.

"The sick are in a hurry to get well, and the friends of the sick are impatient. They will have medicine, and if they do not feel that powerful influence upon their systems their erroneous views lead them to think they should feel, they impatiently change for another physician" (*How to Live*, No. 3, 1865, 2SM 453). Parents, rather than caring for their children with simple treatments, give them drugs instead. "Many parents substitute drugs for judicious nursing" *(Health Reformer,* 1866, Te 85). "It is easier to employ drugs than to use natural remedies" *(Healthful Living,* 1897, *ibid.).*

"The question is, Will they preserve the principles of hygiene, or will they use the easier method of using drugs, to take the place of treating diseases without resorting to drug medication?" (manuscript 22, 1887, 15MR 275).

Used to Circumvent Violations of Health Laws

"The use of natural remedies requires an amount of care and effort that many are not willing to give. Nature's process of healing and upbuilding is gradual, and to the impatient it seems slow. The surrender of hurtful indulgences requires sacrifice" (MH 127). Overcoming unhealthful habits takes courage and sacrifice. "To use drugs while continuing evil habits is certainly inconsistent, and greatly dishonors God by dishonoring the body which He has made" (letter 19, 1892, Te 84).

"When attacked by disease, many will not take the trouble to search out the cause of their illness. Their chief anxiety is to rid themselves of pain and inconvenience. So they resort to patent nostrums, of whose real properties they know little, or they apply to a physician for some remedy to counteract the result of their misdoing, but with no thought of making a change in their unhealthful habits. If immediate benefit is not realized, another medicine is tried, and then another" ([1905] MH 126).

Necessary Drugs That Could Have Been Avoided

Ellen White mentions certain situations that make the use of drugs a necessity but that could have been avoided. "The disuse of meats . . . would place a large number of the sick and suffering ones in a fair way of recovering their health, without the use of drugs. But if the physician encourages a meat-eating diet to his invalid patients, then he will make a necessity for the use of drugs." (manuscript 22, 1887, MM 222). "That which we lack in faith we make up by the use of drugs" (manuscript 169, 1902, 19MR 51).

Summary

Because of the rising death toll of patients receiving treatment from regular physicians using such deadly substances as mercury, arsenic, strychnine, opium, and quinine, medical reformers began to protest the contemporary medical system. They demanded change, but few knew where to turn. Through the years various reformers arose, each with their own "systems of therapy"—homeopaths, Thompsonions, osteopaths, chiropractics, Christian Scientists, and others—but all denouncing drugs in general.

Ellen White's message was clear. While condemning the use of strong, harsh, and poisonous drugs, she suggested that in their place people employ less-harmful remedies and especially emphasized natural agents. She stressed that both the medical profession and the patients must change their health-destroying habits so as to avoid sickness and reduce or eliminate the need for drugs.

In brief, she did not attach herself or her teaching to any reform group, nor did she initiate a reform movement of her own. Her goal was to change the training and practice of regular physicians and nurses and shift the focus of therapy on lifestyle transformation.

Toward the mid-nineteenth century, in the welter of confusion in medicine, health, and religion, God gave to a young untutored woman, Ellen White, counsels and instructions to alter the health and medical practices of her day. Her indictment of regular (allopathic) physicians in the use of powerful drugs, her advocacy of nature's healing powers, her calls for reform in the practice of medicine and of living, eating, and dressing—all came at a time of tremendous need.

References

[1] During the early 1810s Boston's death rate from tuberculosis was 472 per 100,000 inhabitants. By the end of the century it was less than half that number, and then it declined by the mid-1970s to 2 per 100,000. Since then, unfortunately, it has been increasing in certain groups (*Sickness and Health in America: Readings in the History of Medicine and Public Health*, rev. and ed. Judith Leavitt and Ronald Numbers, 3rd ed. [University of Wisconsin Press, 1997], p. 5).

[2] *Ibid.*, p. 3.

[3] A. S. Lyons and R. J. Petrucelli, *Medicine: An Illustrated History*, p. 524.

[4] Richard Dunlop, *Doctors of the American Frontier* (New York: Doubleday and Co., 1965), pp. 1-7, 199.

[5] R. H. Shryock, *Medicine in America*, pp. 206, 207.

[6] W. G. Rothstein, *American Physicians*, p. 44.

[7] *Ibid.*

[8] *Webster's New International Dictionary of the English Language*, 2nd ed.

[9] Rothstein, p. 62.

[10] Shryock, *Medicine in America*, p. 98.

[11] Rothstein, p. 62.

[12] *Ibid.*, p. 50.

[13] *Ibid.*, p. 51.

[14] *Ibid.*, p. 132.

[15] *Ibid.*, p. 54.

[16] A humorist allegedly remarked that "the amount of a medicine one would receive from a homeopathic dose would be the equivalent of dropping one molecule of a drug into the Atlantic Ocean and dosing the patient out of the Pacific."

[17] E. E. Marcy and F. W. Hunt, *The Homeopathic Theory and Practice of Medicine*, Vol. I, pp. vii-xxxii.

[18] *Ibid.*, p. 94.

[19] *Ibid.*, pp. 94-96. Before we leave the subject of mercury, especially calomel, readers might be interested to know that calomel was still a household medicine during my childhood and youth (1914-1935). When I was at Newbold College in England I still occasionally used it. Only when I studied medicine did I realize the drug's poisonous nature.

[20] *Ibid.*, pp. 96-98.

[21] *Ibid.*, pp. 98, 99.

[22] *Ibid.*, p. 99.

[23] *Ibid.*, p. 100.

[24] *Ibid.*

[25] *Ibid.*, p. 104.

[26] I. D. Johnson, *A Guide to Homoeopathic Practice* (Philadelphia: Boericke & Tafel, 1913), p. 19.

[27] Rothstein, pp. 128, 129.

[28] Joseph F. Kett, *The Formation of the American Medical Profession: The Role of Institutions, 1780-1860* (New Haven: Yale University Press, 1968), p. 105.

[29] Lyons and Petrucelli, p. 526.

[30] *Ibid.*

[31] *Ibid.*, pp. 526, 527.

[32] Shryock, *Medicine in America*, pp. 111-125.

[33] *Ibid.*, p. 122.

[34] Dores E. Robinson, *The Story of Our Health Message* (Nashville: Southern Pub. Assn., 1965), pp. 86, 87. (Italics supplied.)

[35] Curtis D. Klaassen, "Principles of Toxicology and Treatment of Poisoning," in Goodman and Gilman, p. 67.

[36] Klaassen, "Heavy Metals and Heavy-Metal Antagonists," in Goodman and Gilman, pp. 1649-1664.

CHAPTER SIX

A Physician Explains . . .

ELLEN WHITE, AN INSTRUMENT OF REFORM

Courage and Foresight

Toward the mid-nineteenth century, in the welter of confusion in medicine and health, God gave to a young untutored woman, Ellen White, counsels and instructions that we can best appreciate when we more fully understand the health and medical practices of her day.

As we have seen, "drug medication," or "drugging," as it was sometimes called, along with bleeding, vomiting, and purging, pervaded the practice of medicine during the early and middle years of Ellen White's life. It was becoming clear, to both physicians and laity alike, that ill-trained practitioners with tradition-bound methods killed more than they cured. Reform was in the air. However, most did not know where to turn, and so joined with the various prominent reformers.

Ellen White attached herself to none of the groups, although she was fully aware of the different positions advocated, nor did she establish a new or different system of medicine, as did most of the other medical reform leaders. She clearly differed from the other reformers in that, while condemning the practice of the times and specifically the use of strong, harsh, poisonous drugs, she had a positive goal toward which she encouraged all reformers to take. It is important to note that she sought to transform both the training and practice of regular medicine, focusing on the use of more physiological remedies and changing the unhealthful, disease-producing habits of the sick to healthful disease-resistant lifestyles.

As medicine and medical education changed, additional divine counsel directed the establishment of medical institutions and the training of nurses and physicians. Thus the denomination started nursing schools and finally a medical school. The medical school was to be "of the highest order," emphasizing in its curriculum the goals set forth above (manuscript 151, 1907, quoted in MM 75). Again, it is worthy to note that the system of medicine to be taught was that of regular medicine[1] but with clearly defined differences.

Meanwhile other reform movements in related areas developed. A number of them came from church organizations—many, for example, requiring abstinence from alcohol, tobacco, tea and coffee, and even encouraging a nonflesh diet. Rush, the master bleeder we mentioned earlier, with one or two others was instrumental in establishing the American Temperance Movement. Within a relatively few years temperance societies sprang up across the United States and spread to most of the countries of Europe.

These drug- health-reforming movements—supported by the advances in the basic sciences of medicine, the discovery of germs, the subsequent development of vaccines, and, as the twentieth century dawned, the isolation of vitamins, minerals, and later hormones—meant that the medicine of the early twentieth century had a face and form far different than when Ellen White started her courageous efforts to change the drugging system of traditional medicine. Gone were the drastics—the strong, harsh, poisonous drugs and the equally deadly procedures of bleeding and purging. Yet her message was still appropriate—the "natural and simple" remedies were the medicines of choice while the use of drugs should be highly selective and employed only when other more physiological measures had failed.

John Harvey Kellogg Comments

In the preface of the book *Christian Temperance and Bible Hygiene* (1890), Dr. John H. Kellogg[2] contrasted Ellen White's teachings with that of other reformers. He stated:

"1. At the time the writings referred to first appeared, the subject of health was almost wholly ignored, not only by the people to whom they were addressed, but by the world at large.

"2. The few advocating the necessity of a reform in physical habits, propagated in connection with the advocacy of genuine reformatory principles the most patent and in some instances disgusting errors.

"3. Nowhere, and by no one, was there presented a systematic and harmonious body of hygienic truths, free from patent errors, and consistent with the Bible and the principles of the Christian religion.

"Under these circumstances, the writings referred to made their appearance. The principles taught were not enforced by scientific authority, but were presented in a simple, straightforward manner by one who makes no pretense to scientific knowledge, but claims to write by the aid and authority of the divine enlightenment.

"How have the principles presented under such peculiar circumstances and with such remarkable claims stood the test of time and experience? . . . The principles which a quarter of a century ago were either entirely ignored or made the butt of ridicule, have quietly won their way into public confidence and esteem, until the world has quite forgotten that they have not always been thus accepted. . . .

"Finally the *reformatory movement* based upon the principles advocated so long ago has lived and prospered until the present time, and the institutions developed by it have grown to be the most extensive and the most prosperous establishments of the sort in the world; while other efforts, looking somewhat in the same direction, but contaminated by error, have either abandoned the principles of truth, and been given over to error, or have fallen into obscurity. . . .

"The guidance of infinite wisdom is as much needed in discerning between truth and error as in the evolution of new truths."[3]

Modern Scientists Evaluate Ellen White as a Reformer

Dr. Jan van Eys,[4] of the University of Texas Medical School, in 1988 reviewed the changing environment of medicine during the latter half of the nineteenth century, and how, during this period, Ellen White wrote most of her counsels. With the emergence of the basic sciences (such as physiological chemistry, microbiology, and experimental physiology) and the growing awareness that human beings and their environment played a role in health and disease, medicine began to recognize that, as then practiced, it was ineffective in its approach to illness.

Van Eys described Ellen White as a social and medical reformer who considered physicians to have a vital role as health educators. "It is not surprising that Ellen White advocated pure air, sunlight, abstemiousness, rest, exercise, proper diet, the use of water, trust in divine power," he observed. "Those, she said, were the true remedies."[5] Contrasting her with Canadian physician, researcher, and medical theorist Sir William Osler, he noted: "There is a real difference . . . between Osler and White. The promises of science were widely acknowledged. Osler had views of science creating direct therapy, whereas Mrs. White accepted science only as a route to improvement of the human lot. Both saw the key to improvement in medical education."[6]

Dr. Clive M. McCay, the late professor emeritus of nutrition at Cornell University and a nutritionist and historian, was greatly impressed by the dietary counsels given through the writings of Ellen White. He taught a graduate course on the history of foods and nutrition. "Among the thousand historical acquaintances in my files, one of the most worth-while is Ellen G. White. As near as one can judge by the evidence of modern nutritional science, her extensive writings on the subject of nutrition, and health in general, are correct in their conclusions."[7] "Mrs. White was a remarkable woman," he commented, "particularly in terms of her health views. I wish, now, to be specific, in support of this statement, by comparing certain of her teachings with present-day well-established facts in nutrition."[8]

He further stated: "Her basic concepts about the relation between diet and health have been verified to an unusual degree by scientific advances of the past decades. Someone may attempt to explain this remarkable fact by saying: 'Mrs. White simply borrowed her ideas from others.' But how would she know which ideas to borrow and which to reject out of the bewildering array of theories and health teachings current in the nineteenth century?

She would have had to be a most amazing person, with knowledge beyond her times, in order to do this successfully!"[9]

Ellen White—A True Reformer

As a reformer she took up the cudgel against the poisonous drugs prevailing at the time. "The inclination to use poisonous drugs, which kill if they do not cure, needs to be guarded against" (manuscript 162, 1897, MM 227). She denounced the practice of a system of medicine that countenanced, used, and promoted such treatments. In 1865 she declared: "Multitude of physicians, and multitude of drugs, have cursed the inhabitants of the earth, and have carried thousands and tens of thousands to untimely graves" *(Health, Or, How to Live,* No. 3, 1865, pp. 49-64, 2SM 450). She encouraged physicians and patients to give nature a chance. "Powerful poisons are often administered which fetter nature in all her friendly efforts to recover from the abuse the system has suffered" *(Health, Or, How to Live,* No. 3, 1865, p. 49, quoted in 2SM 441). And she pointed out that drugs interfere with the body's own healing powers (immune system). "The less there is of drug dosing, the more favorable will be their recovery to health. Drugs, in the place of helping nature, are constantly paralyzing her efforts" (manuscript 22, 1887, quoted in MM 224).

The message that physicians, ministers, teachers, colporteurs, missionaries, and laity were to proclaim was that unhealthful habits result in disease, and that their cure lies in changing these harmful practices rather than treating them with poisonous drugs.

Physicians—First and Foremost Reformers

The major responsibility of physicians was to be leaders in health reform. If they practiced it themselves, their teaching and practice would have a strong influence on their patients. "The first labors of a physician should be to educate the sick and suffering in the very course they should pursue to prevent disease" (manuscript 22, 1887, quoted in MM 221). "Physicians should have wisdom and experience, and be thorough health reformers. Then they will be constantly educating by precept and example their patients from drugs" (*ibid.* 224). She lamented that physicians "prescribe drugs to cure a disease which is the result of indulging unnatural appetites, and two evils are produced in the place of removing one" (*ibid.* 225).

Also she condemned the way in which educational institutions taught medicine. They gave precedence to the symptoms of disease over the functioning of the body (physiology). "When you [a physician] understand physiology in its truest sense, your drug bills will be very much smaller and finally you will cease to deal out drugs at all" (letter 73, 1896, quoted in 2SM 283, 284). Instead, she encouraged physicians to look for the cause of illness. "There is now positive need even with physicians, reformers in the line of treatment of disease, that greater painstaking effort be made to carry forward and upward the work for themselves, and to interestedly instruct those who look to them for medical skill to ascertain the cause of their infirmities" (manuscript 22, 1887, MM 223).

Although she condemned poisonous drugs, she at the same time had a positive goal for medical reforms. "We should correct false habits and practices, and teach the lessons of self-denial" (letter 140, 1909, *ibid.* 85). "Many physicians are not as thorough and intelligent as they ought to be in the practice of their profession. They resort to drugs, when greater skill and knowledge would teach them a more excellent way" (HL 247). What was this more excellent way? She considered it "to educate the sick and suffering in the very course they should pursue to prevent disease" (manuscripts 22, 27, 1887, *ibid.* 221).

People should make changes in their lifestyle: "And when I violate the laws God has established in my being, I am to repent and reform, and place myself in the most favorable condition under the doctors God has provided—pure air, pure water, and the healing, precious sunlight" (letter 35, 1890, *ibid.* 230). "Let them cut away every unhealthful indulgence in eating or drinking. Let them bring their daily practice into harmony with nature's laws" (manuscript 86, 1897, *ibid.* 226, 227). "If the sick and suffering will do only as well as they know in regard to living out the principles of health reform perseveringly, then they will in nine cases out of ten recover from their ailments" (manuscript 22, 1887, *ibid.* 224).

Medical doctors were to be open and frank with their patients. "He [the physician] will, if a reformer, talk plainly in regard to the false appetites and ruinous self-indulgence, in dressing, in eating and drinking, in overtaxing to do a large amount of work in a given time, which has a ruinous influence upon the temper, the physical and mental powers" *(ibid.* 222). "When attacked by disease, many will not take the trouble to search out the cause of their illness. Their chief anxiety is to rid themselves of pain and inconvenience. So they resort to patent nostrums, of whose real properties they know little, or they apply to a physician for some remedy to counteract the result of their misdoing, but with no thought of making a change in their unhealthful habits. If immediate benefit is not realized, another medicine is tried, and then another" (MH 126).

"There is now positive need even with physicians, reformers in the line of treatment for disease. . . . They do not inquire into their former habits of eating and drinking, and take special notice of their erroneous habits which have been for many years laying the foundation of disease. Conscientious physicians should be prepared to enlighten those who are ignorant, and should with wisdom make out their prescriptions, prohibiting those things in their diet which he knows to be erroneous" (manuscript 22, 1887, PC 23). "Right and correct habits, intelligently and perseveringly practiced, will be removing the cause for disease, and the strong drugs need not be resorted to" (MM 222).

Health Reform, a Difficult Task

Ellen White recognized the problems a physician would experience when recommending to a patient a lifestyle change rather than a prescription for a medicine.

"And the work of the physician must begin in an understanding of the works and teachings of the Great Physician. . . . We must cooperate with the Chief of physicians, walking in all humility of mind before Him. Then the Lord will bless our earnest efforts to relieve suffering humanity. It is not by the use of poisonous drugs that this will be done, but by the use of simple remedies. We should seek to correct false habits and practices, and teach the lessons of self-denial" (letter 140, 1909, *ibid.* 85).

"Therefore personal religion for all physicians in the sickroom is essential to success in giving the simple treatment without drugs" (letter 69, 1898, *ibid.* 235).

Nurses

Nurses who believed in lifestyle change and who wished to avoid the use of poisonous drugs were essential in the reformatory movement. "I write these things that you may know that the Lord has not left us without the use of simple remedies which, when used, will not leave the system in the weakened condition in which the use of drugs so often leaves it. We need well-trained nurses who can understand how to use the simple remedies that nature provides for restoration to health, and who can teach those who are ignorant of the laws of health how to use these simple but effective cures" (letter 90, 1908, 2SM 296).

Success in using God's plan, in helping the sick and suffering, requires a close and living association with God. Ellen White said that "this is why the physicians and nurses in our medical institutions should be those who abide in Christ; for through their connection with the heavenly Physician their patients will be blessed. Those God-fearing workers will have no use for poisonous drugs. They will use the natural agencies that God has given for the restoration of the sick" (manuscript 169, 1902, 19MR 50).

Sanitarium-Hospitals and Administrators

The institutions of healing established by the church were to be unique. They were (a) to provide acute care; (b) to provide chronic care; (c) to use natural and simple remedial agencies; and (d) to bring about lifestyle change.

The methods were to be different and designed to influence the practice of medicine. "The light was first given to me why institutions should be established, that is, sanitariums were to reform the medical practices of physicians" (letter 89, 1898, MM 27). They would focus on lifestyle changes and offer distinctive treatments. "The use of drugs has not been specified as in the Lord's order, but

He has given special light concerning our health institutions, directing His people to practice and cultivate hygienic principles" (manuscript 26a, 1892, SpM 7) "Our institutions are established that the sick may be treated by hygienic methods, discarding almost entirely the use of drugs" (manuscript 44, 1896, Te 88).

Medicinal reform was to be an integral part of our medical institutions: "As to drugs being used in our institutions, it is contrary to the light which the Lord has been pleased to give. The drugging business has done more harm to our world and killed more than it has helped or cured" (MM 27). However, even at an early date the problem of drug use was emerging: "The use of poisonous drugs is coming more and more into practice among our people. The light which the Lord has given me is that institutions should be established to do away with drugs, and use God's agencies; that instruction should be given daily upon this subject" (letter 21c, 1892, 20MR 122).

"Among the greatest dangers to our health institutions is the influence of physicians, superintendents, and helpers who profess to believe the present truth, but who have never taken their stand fully upon health reform. . . . Drug medication, as is generally practiced, is a curse" (pamphlet 066, 1896, p. 43, CH 261). "Educate away from drugs. Use them less and less, and depend more upon hygienic agencies" (letter 6a, 1890, MM 259). Here she urged that Adventist physicians and institutions avoid the traditional and routine medicating with drugs, and, whenever and as rapidly as possible, help patients change their unhealthful habits.

Two Interesting Cautions

Drug medication had wide acceptance by both the laity and the medical profession in Ellen White's day. Because of that she cautioned physicians that "you must not always let the patients know that you discard drugs" (letter 182, 1899, 2SM 287).

Referring to Dr. J. H. Kellogg's "largely abolishing the use of drugs" in the Battle Creek Sanitarium, she indicates that he had accomplished this without openly attacking drug medication. Notice her statement: "This work has not been done by making a raid upon drugs, for it needed the wisdom of a serpent and the harmlessness of a dove" (BCL 15 [1899]).

Sanitariums to Have Spiritual Outreach

"Our sanitariums are one of the most successful means of reaching all classes of people. Christ is no longer in this world in person, to go through our cities and towns and villages healing the sick. He has commissioned us to carry forward the medical missionary work. . . . Institutions for the care of the sick are to be established, where men and women may be placed under the care of God-fearing medical missionaries and be treated without drugs" (RH Mar. 23, 1905, CH 212).

Out in the Country

Sanitarium-hospitals were to be rurally located institutions providing a sanctuary for the sick and suffering of both body and soul. "The Lord has shown me that there should be sanitariums near many important cities. . . . Suitable places must be provided to which we can bring the sick and suffering away from the cities, who know nothing of our people, and scarcely anything of Bible truth. Every effort possible is to be made to show the sick that disease may be cured by rational methods of treatment, without having recourse to injurious drugs. Let the sick be separated from harmful surroundings and associations, and placed in our sanitariums, where they can receive treatment from Christian nurses and physicians, and thus they become acquainted with the Word of God" (letter 63, 1905, Ev 534).

The location of our sanitariums was most important. They should be within easy reach of population centers, yet in an environment in which the patients could appreciate nature and nature's God. "Let the leaders in our work instruct the people that sanitariums should be established in the midst of the most pleasant surroundings, in places not disturbed by the turmoil of the city, places where by wise instruction the thoughts of the patients can be bound up with the thoughts of God" ([1902] 7T 81).

Such institutions should possess a serene atmosphere of caring, a pervasive atmosphere of kindness and love. The religion of the administrators and staff must be from the heart. "It is expected that there shall stand at the head of our sanitariums men who labor in harmony with God because they receive wisdom daily from His word; men of prayer, men who realize their accountability to guard the religious interests of every young man and woman employed in the institution. . . . Our sanitariums should be safeguards to our youth" (letter 148, 1906, 7MR 301).

"Thus in simple language we may teach the people how to preserve health, how to avoid sickness. This is the work our sanitariums are called upon to do. This is true science" (manuscript 105, 1898, SpM 137).

The preceding quotations depict a hospital/health retreat far different from our present concrete-and-steel institutions located in large city complexes. I recall spending three days in an intensive coronary-care unit (it turned out that I didn't need to be there!). It had no TV, no radio, no visitors, no reading, not even the Bible! Only my own morbid thoughts centering on my possible problems. What if I had been wheeled outside into a garden and watched the bees at work, or the butterflies skipping from one flower to another, and heard the birds singing and the breeze blowing through the trees? It would take courage to design such an acute-care unit today, but it would be leading the way.

The College of Medical Evangelists (Now Loma Linda University)

One of the goals God showed Ellen White was the establishment of a medical school that would surround its students with a spiritual and self-sacrificing atmosphere. "The medical school at Loma Linda is to be of the highest order, because those who are in that school have the privilege of maintaining a living connection with the wisest of all physicians, from whom there is communicated knowledge of a superior order" (*Pacific Union Recorder*, Feb. 3, 1910, MM 57). It would emphasize lifestyle change for both the students and their patients and replace standard drug therapy with natural and simple remedies. "The students at Loma Linda are seeking for an education that is after the Lord's order, an education that will help them to develop into successful teachers and laborers for others. . . . Our people should become intelligent in the treatment of sickness without the aid of poisonous drugs" (manuscript 15, 1911, *ibid.* 56, 57).

Loma Linda should teach practicing physicians that the primary therapy should not be on drugs but simpler remedies. "I found an article that I had written about a year ago, in reference to the establishment of a school of the highest order, in which the students would not be taught to use drugs in the treatment of the sick" (letter 360, 1907, LLM 309).

Again she wrote: "Let the students be given a practical education. . . . Special instruction should be given in the art of treating the sick without the use of poisonous drugs and in harmony with the light that God has given. In the treatment of the sick, poisonous drugs need not be used" (manuscript 39, 1909, 9T 175, 176).

The quality of training that Loma Linda would offer would be such that its graduates would not need to learn the methods of schools that stressed treatment revolving around drug therapy. "Some of our medical missionaries have supposed that a medical training according to the plans of worldly schools is essential to their success. . . . I would now say, Put away such ideas. . . . The principles of health reform brought into the life of the patient, the use of natural remedies, and the cooperation of divine agencies in behalf of the suffering, will bring success" (letter B-61, 1910, RH Mar. 6, 1913).

God's Blessings Essential

The treatment offered at Loma Linda, however, would fail without the blessings of God. "We must cooperate with the Chief of physicians, walking in all humility of mind before Him. Then the Lord will bless our earnest efforts to relieve suffering humanity. It is not by the use of poisonous drugs that this will be done, but by the use of simple remedies. We should seek to correct false habits and practices, and teach the lessons of self-denial" (letter 140, 1909, MM 85).

"It would have been better if those sent from our schools to Ann Arbor[10] had never had any connection with that institution.

The education in drug medication and the false religious theories have brought forth a class of practitioners who need to unlearn much they have learned. They need to obtain an altogether different experience before they can say in word and in deed, We are medical missionaries" (letter 3, 1901, 17MR 91).

Living healthfully was a program to which few subscribed. People feared night air and shut out sunlight in their homes, and poorly understood and rarely practiced personal and environmental cleanliness. Through the years, for reasons it is still difficult to understand, medical education has failed to include in its curriculum the importance of a healthy lifestyle. Today, as we enter a new millennium, well-documented research has established beyond a doubt that unhealthy lifestyles lie at the root of most of the killer diseases seen in the developed countries of the world. But modern medical education spends little time and only token emphasis on training physicians that it is their obligation to evaluate the patient's lifestyle, and to instruct why and how patients should correct unhealthful habits. Many claim that physicians are too busy to take time to educate their patients. If so, other trained professionals could provide the necessary instruction. Medicine should add them to its team.

A little reflection will show that lifestyle diseases are also the major killers in developing nations of the world. In large populations of the earth, both city and rural, contaminating the water and soil from human wastes is almost a way of life. As a result, the incidence of and mortality from infection soars.

An Outline of Ellen White's Reforms

Instead of organizing a new or different system of medicine, Ellen White sought to reform the training and practice of regular medicine. In brief, here is Ellen White's reform message: she (a) condemned the use of poisonous drugs or "drugging"; (b) denounced the way her time practiced medicine; (c) urged that physicians should be educators, adopting a healthful lifestyle themselves and encouraging patients to do the same; (d) stressed that every member of the church adopt and promote a healthful lifestyle; (e) recommended the establishment of sanitariums (medical institutions) that encouraged preventive health practices; (f) advised the organization of schools of nursing associated with our medical institutions; (g) instructed that the denomination start a four-year school of medicine; and finally (h) counseled that every member of the church—whether minister, teacher, or layperson—reform their own lifestyle, thus becoming a model to all who would listen.

Medical practice in her day, with rare exceptions, focused on drug therapy. When a patient was sick, physicians, as they examined the patient, immediately thought of what drugs they should prescribe. No consideration of lifestyle change entered their minds. As a consequence Ellen White condemned poisonous drugs as the primary objective of therapy and cautioned against even the use of less harmful remedies because it distracted them from preventative medicine. She sought to redirect medicine to lifestyle change, establishing medical institutions in which lifestyle change predominated. Also she saw medical/health teachings as an entering wedge for evangelism.

Even today, though, much of medicine still heavily stresses drug therapy, and Seventh-day Adventist medical institutions, in general, operate as acute-care facilities. We give too little thought and effort toward lifestyle change. What do the counsels of the Lord instruct us to do? Consider the following:

1. Fortunately, medical science has discarded the old poisonous drugs.

2. Generally, new less-harmful drugs more carefully target specific problems.

3. Physicians, however, still need to remember the potentials for long-term lifestyle change even as they examine the patient and consider short-term therapy.

4. Lifestyle change, wherever applicable, should be the first choice of the physician, particularly in long-term therapy.

5. Seventh-day Adventist medical institutions need to be leaders in advocating and using lifestyle change, wherever and whenever appropriate.

6. The Seventh-day Adventist Church must embrace the message of lifestyle transformation, and use it much more as an avenue of approach in its God-given mission to the world.

The following table attempts to outline the differences between the regular practice of medicine, with its focus on drug therapy, and a concept of medicine that stresses lifestyle change. The tools of the former system were drugs, while the instruments of the latter should be the natural, simple, and least harmful remedies.

The Practice of Medicine—Then and Now			
Period	**The Patient**	**Diagnosis**	**Focus of Therapy**
1850-1900	Treated with disrespect	Generally unknown	Relief of symptoms
		Drugs— Powerful, strong, harsh, poisonous: mercury, arsenic, opium	Procedures— Bloodletting, purging, vomiting, blistering, dehydration, loss of critical body fluids
Ellen White's Goals 1865—	Treated with respect— God's creation	"Cause to effect"	Lifestyle change
		Remedies— natural, simple, less harmful "to tide one over"	Lifestyle change— unhealthful habits to be overcome
Today and into the twenty-first century	Treated with respect	Every attempt to pinpoint accuracy	Cure of illness.
		Remedies— drugs, precisely selected, carefully targeted, less harmful	Lifestyle change— incidental

Remedies Classified

A careful analysis of Ellen White's writings would suggest that she divided remedies (medicines and procedures) into four major groups:

1. Natural Remedies
2. Herbal Remedies
3. Simple Remedies
4. Drugs and Mixtures

Let us now carefully consider each group of therapeutic agents.

References

[1] Regular medicine, or orthodox medicine, was the traditional system of medical practice. Hahnemann, one of the early leaders in the reform movement, contrasted his concept of homeopathy with regular medicine, which he called allopathy. Thus many divided medical practitioners into homeopaths and allopaths.

[2] Kellogg received his medical degree from Bellevue Hospital Medical College in New York, one of the better medical schools of the time. He took advanced studies at Bellevue and at institutions in Europe. Besides being an eloquent speaker, he was a notable researcher in medicine and foods. With his brother William K. he virtually initiated the breakfast industry. Through his efforts and the blessing of God he built Battle Creek Sanitarium and Hospital into a world-renowned institution. The words "Battle Creek" became a symbol of health, and the rich and important flocked to its doors. It spawned similar institutions throughout the world (see Richard W. Schwarz, *John Harvey Kellogg, M.D.* (Nashville: Southern Pub. Assn., 1970), pp. 30-34.

[3] Ellen G. and James White, *Christian Temperance and Bible Hygiene* (Battle Creek, Mich.: Good Health Publishing Co., 1890), pp. iii, iv.

[4] Dr. Jan van Eys is a graduate of the University of Washington. At the time he wrote his article he was Mosbacher Chair in Pediatrics, head of the Division of Pediatrics, and chair of the Departments of Pediatrics and Experimental Pediatrics at the University of Texas' M. D. Anderson Hospital and Tumor Institute. Now semiretired, he lives in Tennessee and teaches part-time at the medical school at Vanderbilt University. He is a member of the United Methodist Church. In a letter to the author he stated that his denominational affiliation "does not preclude me from admiring many of Ellen White's insights on the intersection of social conditions and medical problems" (letter to author, May 10, 1999).

[5] Jan van Eys, "Modern Medicine and Old Dilemmas," *The Pharos* 51 (Fall 1988): 30.

[6] *Ibid.*

[7] Clive M. McCay, "A Nutrition Authority Discusses Mrs. White," *Review and Herald*, Feb. 12, 1959.

[8] ———, "Science Confirms Our Health Teachings," *Review and Herald*, Feb. 19, 1959.

[9] ———, "Our Health Teachings Further Confirmed," *Review and Herald*, Feb. 26, 1959.

[10] Ellen White had in mind the medical school at the University of Michigan.

CHAPTER SEVEN

A Physician Explains . . .

NATURAL REMEDIES

Whenever discussing the treatment of illness or disease, Ellen White suggested using "natural" and "simple remedies" as preferable to "drugs." What are "natural remedies"?

Natural Remedies

Ellen White used a number of expressions to describe "natural remedies." They included "true remedies," "nature's remedies," "God's remedies," "heaven-sent remedies," "God's appointed remedies," and "God's medicines." She identified them in the statement "Pure air, sunlight, abstemiousness, rest, exercise, proper diet, the use of water, trust in divine power—these are the true remedies" ([1905] MH 127).

Such natural remedies should be the agents of choice in treating disease for a number of reasons. Besides being physiologically necessary for health, some are absolutely essential for life itself. We tend to take for granted air, water, and food as we breathe, drink, and eat. The remaining five vary according to the circumstances of life—when and how much we sleep, the extent to which we expose ourselves to sunlight, whether or not we engage in any form of exercise, the degree to which we avoid harmful indulgences, and the role that divine power may play in our lives.

Yet all are vital in maintaining health and strengthening the body's resistance against illness and disease. Practiced within physiological limits—not too little or too much—they can do no harm

Ailment	Natural Remedy or Medication
Constipation	free use of water and unrefined foods (high in fiber), providing a moist generous stool
	or (a.) the use of botanic drugs: senna, cascara, etc.; (b.) the use of regular drugs: laxatives, cathartics
Insomnia	exercise to relax muscle tension and provide physiological fatigue, and trust in God's watchcare to remove anxiety will induce sound, restful sleep
	or (a.) the use of botanic drugs: hop; (b.) the use of regular drugs: sleeping pills
Rickets	appropriate exposure to sunlight and a diet rich in calcium (green leafy vegetables and whole-grain cereals)
	or vitamin supplements (especially D and calcium)
Osteoporosis	exercise to produce a physiological demand for strong well-mineralized bones, and a good nutritious diet (provide adequate calcium and other minerals)
	or calcium lactate supplements plus hormones
Chronic fatigue	adequate rest and sleep, along with appropriate exercise and trust in God's watchcare over us
	or the use of medications: relaxants, pep pills
Type II Diabetes (adult onset)	a diet high in unrefined carbohydrates (sugars, starches, and fiber), low in fat, moderate in protein, within desirable caloric limits (sometimes requiring continued use of limited insulin intake)
	or insulin with possible undesirable consequences

but only good. Their judicious use has no toxic or side effects!

The "eight natural remedies" actually embody the very foundations of life and health. Let us now carefully examine this oft-quoted statement: "Pure air, sunlight, abstemiousness, rest, exercise, proper diet, the use of water, trust in divine power—

114

these are the true remedies" (MH 127 [1905]).

Pure air and water (free from chemical and particulate contamination), adequate exercise and rest, a nutritious diet, appropriate exposure to sunshine (but protecting the skin from overexposure), avoidance of excesses, deficiencies, and health-destroying habits such as smoking, drinking, and illicit drugging, and freedom from emotional stress obtained by trust in divine power—all are the fundamental physiological laws on which a healthful lifestyle rests.

Such physiological principles are preventive, and become remedies only when ignored or violated. Here are a few examples of how we might employ them, remedially coupled with ways traditional medicine might treat the problem.

Proper Diet

One of the eight natural remedies is diet. Just what is a proper diet? What kinds of food would comprise it?

Plants, as we have already pointed out, are chemical structures. A common leaf, whether it be cabbage, lettuce, or some nonfood source such as the tobacco plant, consists of some 1,000 different chemicals. Such chemicals include the traditional nutrients that provide the substances we need in our food—proteins, carbohydrates (sugars, starches, and fiber), fats, vitamins, and minerals. In recent years medical science has discovered a large class of biologically active chemicals—scores if not hundreds—present in food plants. By that we mean that they play a role in the body's functioning. Researchers have called them nonnutritive food components, or phytochemicals, and have designated those that have been at least partially isolated and purified as nutriceuticals.

A paper published by *Vegetarian Nutrition,* a practice group of the American Dietetic Association, entitled "Phytochemicals to Protect Our Health," begins: "A diet characterized by a frequent consumption of vegetables, fruit, whole-grain cereals, and legumes with some nuts and seeds represents the optimal diet for good health."[1] They observe that "the National Cancer Institute has identified about three dozen plant foods that possess significant cancer-protective properties, including garlic, onions, soybeans, ginger, licorice root, the umbelliferous vegetables (including carrots, celery, cilantro, parsley), flax seed, citrus, turmeric, cruciferous vegetables (broccoli, brussels sprouts, cabbage and cauliflower), tomatoes, peppers, brown rice, oats, whole wheat, herbs of the mint family (rosemary, thyme, oregano, sage, basil), cucumber, cantaloupe and berries. Scientists have identified a variety of cancer-protective phytochemicals in these foods."[2]

Many of these and other phytochemical-containing foods play a significant preventive role, and at times have a curative effect in cancers (mentioned above); cardiovascular diseases: coronary heart disease, cardiac arrhythmias, hypertension, hyperlipedemia (lowering blood cholesterol), and diabetes, to mention just a few examples.

A recent article in the *Canadian Journal of Dietetic Practice and Research* speaks of a number of common foods as being rich in beneficial phytochemicals. "Citrus, in addition to its ample supply of vitamin C, folic acid, potassium and pectin, contains a host of active phytochemicals that also protect our health. In fact, there are over 170 phytochemicals in an orange. There are over 60 flavonoids in citrus; their range of properties includes anti-inflammatory and antitumor activity, inhibition of blood clots and strong antioxidant activity."[3]

"Plant foods are rich in a wide variety of phytochemicals which have been linked to reduced risk for chronic disease. This underscores the importance of building diets around an abundance of whole plant foods including vegetables, fruits, whole grains, legumes, nuts and seeds. For optimal health, one should consume at least five to nine servings per day of fruits and vegetables, six or more servings of grains (including at least three servings of whole grains), and two or three servings of legumes, nuts and/or seeds."[4]

Such foods must not be merely an adjunct to a traditional Western diet with its high animal protein, fat, and refined carbohydrates, such as refined cereals, sugar-laden foods, and soft drinks. A proper diet *must be* from whole foods that God designed for us to eat—fruits, grains, nuts, and vegetables.

We need to understand clearly that good, wholesome food is the greatest medicine of all! Look at the diseases that food has been the cure of for more than the past 100 years: scurvy, beriberi, pellagra, kwashiorkor, marasmus, night blindness, rickets, anemias,

Phytochemicals Found in Different Plant Foods[5]

Phytochemical	Food Source
anthocyanidins	grapes, raspberries, blueberries, cherries
carotenoids	yellow-orange vegetables and fruits; green leafy vegetables; red fruits
catechins	green tea
chalcones	licorice
coumarins	carrots, caraway, celery, parsley
curcumins	turmeric, ginger
diallyl sulfide disulfides, trisulfides	onions, garlic, chives, leeks
dithiolthiones	cruciferous vegetables
ellagic acid	grapes, strawberries, raspberries, nuts
flavinoids	most fruits and vegetables
glucarates	citrus, grains, tomatoes, bell peppers
indoles, isothiocyantes	broccoli, cabbage, cauliflower, radish
isoflavones	soybeans, tofu
lignans	soybeans, flax seed, sesame
liminoids	citrus
phenolic acids	berries, grapes, nuts, whole grains
phthalides, polyacetylenes	caraway, celery, cumin, dill, fennel, parsley
phytates	grains, legumes
phytosterols	nuts, seeds, legumes
saponins	beans, herbs, licorice root
terpenoids	cherries, citrus, herbs (such as basil, oregano, thyme, sage, rosemary)

and so forth. The finding of the phytochemicals and their role in our welfare merely indicates our previous ignorance. God, when He created food on the third day of Creation, knew what all living creatures, including humanity, required for health and disease. *A proper diet is a "medicine" that has no side effects.*

In the mail I received an announcement from the American College of Nutrition of a symposium to be held on advances in clinical nutrition. Here are a few titles of the papers that would be presented: "Phytonutrient Update: An Overview"; "Soybeans and Cancer"; "Nuts and Health: Clinical Trials"; "Whole Grains and Cancer"; "Whole Grains and Heart Disease"; "Whole Grain Components and Health"; and the list goes on.

Dr. Winston Craig, writing in the *Journal of the American Dietetic Association,* concludes an article entitled "Phytochemicals: Guardians of Our Health" by observing that "the protective benefits of a phytochemical-rich diet is best obtained from frequent consumption of fruits, vegetables, and whole grain products."[6]

Other Natural Remedies

Notice some of the many benefits from using nature's true remedies. Here are a few examples.

"Nature will want some assistance to bring things to their proper condition, which may be found in the simplest remedies, especially in the use of nature's own furnished remedies—pure air, and with a precious knowledge of how to breathe; pure water, with a knowledge of how to apply it; plenty of sunlight in every room in the house if possible, and with an intelligent knowledge of what advantages are to be gained by its use. All these are powerful in their efficiency, and the patient who has obtained a knowledge of how to eat and dress healthfully may live for comfort, for peace, for health" (manuscript 22, 1887, MM 223, 224).

"In the efforts made for the restoration of the sick to health, use is to be made of the beautiful things of the Lord's creation. . . . The flowers, . . . the ripe fruit, . . . the happy songs of the birds, have a peculiarly exhilarating effect on the nervous system. By the influence of the quickening, reviving, life-giving properties of nature's great medicinal resources, the functions of the body are strengthened, the intellect awakened, the imagination quickened, the spirits enlivened. The mind is prepared to appreciate the beauties of God's word" (letter 71, 1902, *ibid.* 231).

"Life in the open air is good for body and mind. It is God's medicine for the restoration of health. Pure air, good water, sunshine, beautiful surroundings—these are His means for restoring the sick to health in natural ways" (manuscript 41, 1902, *ibid.* 233).

"Nature is God's physician. The pure air, the glad sunshine, the beautiful flowers and trees, the orchards and vineyards, and outdoor exercise amid these surroundings, are health-giving—the elixir of life" ([1902] 7T 76).

"There are life-giving properties in the balsam of the pine, in the fragrance of the cedar and the fir, and other trees also have properties that are health restoring" (MH 264).

"The more the patient can be kept out of doors, the less care will he require. . . . Surround him with the beautiful things of nature; place him where he can see the flowers growing and hear the birds singing, and his heart will break into song in harmony with the songs of the birds. Relief will come to body and mind" (*ibid.* 265).

"Good deeds are twice a blessing, benefiting both the giver and the receiver of the kindness. The consciousness of right-doing is one of the best medicines for diseased bodies and minds" (*ibid.* 257).

"If those who are suffering from ill-health would forget self in their interest for others; if they would fulfill the Lord's command to minister to those more needy than themselves, they would realize the truthfulness of the prophetic promise, 'Then shall thy light break forth as the morning, and thine health shall spring forth speedily'" (*ibid.* 258).

"Plans should be devised for keeping patients out of doors. For those who are able to work, let some pleasant, easy employment be provided" (*ibid.* 264).

Where and When Effective

The natural remedies treat lifestyle diseases, that is, diseases resulting from one's environment or habits of life. Such diseases may differ according to whether one lives in a developed or underdeveloped nation. Examples of some common lifestyle diseases include:

Developed nations

Chronic vascular diseases (atherosclerotic vessels): coronary heart disease and stroke. They result from diets high in animal fats, refined carbohydrates, and low in dietary fiber, and from stress-filled lives with little or no exercise.

Cancer: the way people choose to live increases the risk, especially tobacco and marijuana smoking, and diets high in animal fat and low in antioxidants, dietary fiber, and plant foods.

Chronic kidney disease: diets requiring the kidney to work excessively—those high in protein and in minerals, especially salt, overtax the organ.

Emphysema: smoke-filled environments damage the lungs.

Hypertension: stress, anxiety, and a high-salt diet raise the blood pressure.

Diabetes: prolonged intake of refined sugar will lead to Type II.

Obesity: a sedentary lifestyle causes the pounds to accumulate.

Underdeveloped nations

Many of the developing areas of the world have a different set of diseases. Such diseases involve both the physical environment in which the people live and, as in the developed world, their own life habits.

Infectious diseases

Waterborne—intestinal parasites: worms, amoeba, typhoid fever, cholera, etc.

Soilborne—worms.

Insect-borne—malaria, sleeping sickness, dengue fever, typhus.

Foodborne—diarrhea, dysentery.

Physical contact—leprosy.

Sexually transmitted—AIDS, gonorrhea, syphilis, venereal herpes.

Nutritionally Related

Beriberi—lack of B vitamins because of refined rice, corn, wheat
Pellagra—lack of B vitamins because of refined rice, corn, wheat
Night blindness—lack of vitamin A
Kwashiorkor—diet, mainly refined carbohydrates in infants and children
Marasmus—starvation in infants
Scurvy—lack of vitamin C

Nonnutritionally Related

Cancers: mouth (chewing *pan,* composed of betel leaf or nut, with tobacco and lime).

As we discuss the natural remedies, we must recognize that the glimpses of what modern therapeutics may provide in the future increasingly support what the Lord has revealed through Ellen White regarding this subject. The knowledgeable use of such remedies is the goal she sets before the faithful physician. "There are many ways of practicing the healing art, but there is only one way that Heaven approves. God's remedies are the simple agencies of nature" (5T 443). As we proceed in the following chapters to study what the Lord and science have revealed, may God give each reader a wise and understanding heart.

Summary

Regardless of where we live—rural, town, or inner city, in developed or developing nations—the environment in which we live and our own habits of life, together with our individual hereditary patterns, determine the diseases to which we will fall heir.

God's "natural remedies" are remedies only if we are not utilizing them or living in harmony with them. They treat diseases resulting from an unhealthful lifestyle and/or an unhealthful environment. Today medical science calls such conditions "lifestyle diseases." Adoption of the principles underlying the natural remedies is the only means of changing an unhealthful lifestyle to a healthy one.

Ideally we will live such a life in an environment that controls disease-producing insects; that has uncontaminated air, water, and soil; that allows us to work and exercise safely outdoors in the sunshine; that has adequate, wholesome, and safe food; that helps us avoid unhealthful habits; that lets trust in God bring healthful relaxation, rest, and sleep; that provides satisfying and stress-free employment; that encourages us to devote life to the worship of God and service to fellow humanity; and that, when possible, surrounds us with the things of God's creation—mountains and plains, streams and lakes, trees and flowers, birds and animals—to enjoy with loved ones and friends.

Where in this world is such a life possible? And if such a place exists, isn't it out of reach to most mortals? Still, our responsibility is to strive toward such a life, for it will bring health to body, mind, and soul; prevent or delay the onset of illness and aging; and provide a contented, longer, and higher quality of life. It will also prepare us to meet our Creator and Redeemer, who has gone to prepare just such a place for you and for me.

References

[1] "Phytochemicals to Protect Our Health," a paper published by Vegetarian Nutrition, a dietetic practice group of the American Dietetic Association, 1998.

[2] *Ibid.*

[3] Winston Craig and Leslie Beck, "Phytochemicals: Health Protective Effects," *Canadian Journal of Dietetic Practice and Research* 60, No. 2 (1999): 80.

[4] "Phytochemicals to Protect Our Health."

[5] *Ibid.*

[6] Winston J. Craig, "Phytochemicals: Guardians of Our Health," *Journal of the American Dietetic Association* 97, No. 10 (October 1997): S203.

CHAPTER EIGHT

A Physician Explains . . .

HERBAL REMEDIES[1]

SECTION I

S omeone once said that there are but two types of fools: one professes 'This is old and therefore is good,' and the other says, 'This is new and therefore better.'

"But when judging the medical value of the information regarding plants, neither view has a scientific basis."[2]

A Point to Ponder

From a human perspective plants fall into four categories: food plants, plants that are inedible because of taste or odor, medicinal plants, and poisonous plants. The ability to distinguish one from the other requires long study and great wisdom, especially when it comes to the latter two.

The Creator made plants great chemists. The vast and magnificent diversity seen in nature indirectly attests to the multitude of chemicals that make such plant structures possible. When closely examined, every leaf and flower, every stem and root, may possess a chemical that might prove to be a blessing or a curse (when misused).[3]

The Background of Herbal Medicine

As sickness and disease arose in the world, human beings looked for relief from their suffering. By experimenting with plants they found some that appeared to be beneficial. Succeeding generations continued to use them, and in time people began to write about them. The oldest botanical documents come from the ancient Near East, India, and China.

In India Ayurvedic (knowledge of life) medicine arose from four books, the Vedas. They identify three elements, called doshas, that pervade all nature. The doshas affect the body, mind, personality, and health of an individual. Imbalance in one or other of the doshas results in sickness and disease. Ayurvedic medicine believes that the natural world has varying types of plants with specific properties. When a person becomes ill, wisely selected plants will provide the specific needs of the sick one, bringing about a balance among the doshas. Restoring the balance brings healing and health.[4]

In China another system of medicine developed. The Chinese believed that two forces existed in all forms of life, yin and yang, and that an imbalance in the opposing forces results in illness and disease. They also believed that health depends on a vital energy, called *qi* (chi). An imbalance in a person's *qi* can, in turn, upset the balance of his or her yin and yang, causing illness. We can use the vital energy or *qi* in plants to balance the yin and yang for healing and health. The physician (herbalist) carefully selects medicinal plants to meet the specific needs of the patient. A number of books, some dating back thousands of years before Christ, record the descriptions and use of hundreds of medicinal plants. Two well-known plant substances from China are ephedra (mahuang) and ginseng (panax).[5]

Archaeological findings show that the ancient Egyptians collected quite a bit of knowledge about medicinal plants. Discovered by a German Egyptologist, the Ebers papyrus is probably the most well-known record of such medical plants and preparations, dating back to approximately 1500 B.C.[6]

In the Middle East the Code of Hammurabi was one of the earliest known guidelines on the practice of medicine.[7] Thousands of years later Avicenna, or Ibn Sina (A.D. 980-1037), known as the "Prince of the Physicians" in eastern Persia, methodically codified a whole system of medicine. History credits him as being the first to distill essential oils from plants. A prolific writer, his best-known book is the *Cannon of Medicine,* and his botanic remedies influenced Europe for hundreds of years.

Medicine developed and flourished in ancient Greece as society established schools to train physicians. Many consider Hippocrates (c. 460-370 B.C.), the son of a physician, as the father of medicine. Aristotle (384-322 B.C.) wrote a book entitled *De Plants*, in which he describes some 500 plants. Others through the centuries compiled lists of medicinal herbs that became known as Materia Medicas.[8]

Galen, a Greek physician of the second century A.D., was a prolific writer. Among his many publications was an herbal called *De Simplicus*. He is famous for a mixture he developed named theriac. It consisted of medicinal herbs, animal tissues, minerals, and also contained opium, wine, and honey. Through the years other physicians added other ingredients so by the nineteenth century it contained more than 200 ingredients![9]

During the Middle Ages the monastic orders of the Catholic Church preserved many of the ancient herbal records. Then with the start of the Renaissance (fifteenth and sixteenth centuries) scholars began to study these books and manuscripts. Pharmacopeias, or books describing the properties and formulations of medications, with their suggested uses, came off the press from time to time in France and other European countries. Britain published John Gerard's herbal in 1597.

As we might expect, immigrants from all over Europe transported English and European medicine to America. Many brought with them seeds and plants used for food and medicine. The early settlers also adopted Native American medical practices. People commonly used medicinal herbs, and many homes had a family herbal.

During the early and middle years of the nineteenth century a revulsion to the orthodox practice of medicine grew both among the medical profession and the laity. Bloodletting, blistering, and other harsh methods of depleting a patient's body fluids, while forbidding the drinking of water, resulted in a renewed interest in what nature had to offer. It gave rise to the eclectics, physicians who employed less drastic treatments and attempted to emphasize herbal medicines. However, the emerging disciplines of anatomy, physiology, biochemistry, microbiology, pharmacology, and pathology caused the interest in eclectic medicine to fade gradually.[10]

The Nature of Botanic Medicine

We have had a brief glimpse of the role medicinal herbs have played through the centuries. As we enter the next millennium we again see a growing interest in herbal medicine. How long it will last and how large it will grow time alone will tell. With this brief background, let us examine the properties of medicinal herbs or botanic drugs, and attempt to determine the role they played in treating the illnesses and diseases prevalent in Ellen White's time and even, perhaps, obtain insights into how they might be of use in medicine today.

To simplify the discussion of medicinal herbs, the term *plant* or *herb* will include any or all of its parts unless otherwise stated.

In the seventeenth and nineteenth centuries herbalists divided medicines into "singles"—later called "simples," referring to a single herb—and "mixtures." Those who collected plants for medicine acquired the name "simplers" (see chapter 3).

Examples of Medicinal Herbs

Webster calls a simple "a vegetable drug."[11] In our discussion we will refer to all such medicinal products as botanic drugs to distinguish them from the regular drugs used by physicians. Botanic drugs are plants or plant parts and may be taken fresh, dried, or as a powder, extract, or tincture. A medicinal herb may be the whole plant, or a part of the plant, such as the flower, fruit, leaf, stem, rhizome, root, bulb, bark, sap, trunk and branches, or a substance extracted from the plant or plant part. Here are a few examples:[12]

Flowers:	Red clover blossoms, dried *(Trifolium pratense),* used as a tea, having a tealike aroma and slightly sweetish in taste. It is the ingredient of anti-asthmatic cigarettes, and some consider it to have no medicinal virtue.
Fruit:	Capsicum is the dried ground fruit of cayenne

pepper or red pepper *(Capsicun frutescens* and vari-
eties). The pepper's active ingredients are capsaicin,
a volatile alkaloid, and fixed oils. People have
used it externally as a rubefacient (reddening the
skin by increasing local circulation), internally as a
stimulant, and for sore throat as a gargle.

Seeds: Castor oil is expressed from the seeds of the castor
oil plant *(Ricinus communis)*. Digestion releases its
active ingredient, ricinoleic acid, employed as a
cathartic and sometimes as an emetic. The seed,
however, contains a powerful poison called ricin.

Leaves: Foxglove leaves *(Digitalis purpurea)* contain the
active ingredients (glucosides) digitoxin, digitonin,
digitalin, digitalein, gitalin, and digitin. Administered in acute circulatory failure, they will strengthen
the action of the heart.

Bark: Bark from the cinchona tree, or Peruvian bark
(Cinchona ledgeriana Moens, *C. calisaya* Wedell,
C. officialis, and hybrids) contains the alkaloids
quinine, quinidine, and others. People have long
used it to treat malaria, as a bitter in certain drinks
to increase appetite, to relieve muscle cramps, and
to slow the heart.

Sap: Opium, the dried exudation from the immature
head of a poppy *(Papaver somniferum),* has the
active ingredients (alkaloids) morphine, codeine,
papaverine. They will relieve severe pain and will
act as a sedative and an antidiarrheal agent.

**Rhizome
and roots:** Goldenseal is the powdered dry rhizomes and roots
of *Hydrastis canadensis.* Its active ingredients
(alkaloids), hydrastine and berberine, act as a local
astringent.

**Trunk and
branches:** Camphor derives from the trunk, root, and branches
of the camphor tree *(Cinnamomum camphora).* The
active ingredients—cymol, camphoric acid, volatile
oils, and alcohols—serve as a stimulant and anti-

spasmodic. Also people have employed it externally as a rubefacient.

How Herbs Are Taken as Medication

Generally people take medicinal herbs by mouth. The most common ways include (a) finely cut pieces or powders with small, medium, or coarse particles, (b) teas in which the herb is steeped in water, (c) fluidextract, "an alcohol preparation of a vegetable drug containing the active constituents of one gram of the dry drug in each milliliter,"[13] (d) tincture, a solution of a medicinal preparation in alcohol, usually expressed in percents: 5 percent, 8 percent, 10 percent, etc.

Two examples of medicinal herbs taken in extract form are catnip and hops tea. The first consists of a tea made from catnip, the dried leaves and flowering tops of *Nepeta cataria).* Catnip's active ingredients are of a volatile oil and tannin. People have used the plant for calming the stomach, as a stimulant, for a tonic, and as a sweating agent. The second example is a tea made from the dried fruit or strobiles of hops *(Humulus lupulus).* Its active ingredients are of a volatile oil, lupulin, and tannins, and herbalists have long employed it for dyspepsia, as a sedative, and for insomnia.

The Properties of a Medicinal Herb

A medicinal herb is a plant or a preparation derived from a plant believed to possess healing properties. The presence in the plant tissues of one or more chemicals possessing a healing property distinguishes a medicinal herb from other plants.

A plant may contain a thousand or more different chemicals to maintain its structure and fulfill its functions. Such chemicals include proteins, sugars and starches, fats and oils, fiber, vitamins, minerals, phytochemicals, antioxidants, and other biologically active compounds. As we mentioned earlier, we refer to this general class of chemicals as nutrients, because they play an extremely important role in our diet. But beyond them are hundreds of other substances the plant needs to exist. Such chemicals vary from one part of the plant to another, making the flower different from the fruit, the fruit from the seeds, the seeds from the leaves, and the leaves from the bark, stem, or roots.

When we eat a plant or any one of its parts, digestion releases its chemical components. Some of them the body will absorb, others it will not. If no harm results, and its flavor and odor are acceptable, we consider the plant a food.

Many nonfood plants contain chemicals, apart from nutrients, that produce biological actions that may be either desirable or harmful. If harmful, we regard them as poisonous plants. But should the action be considered beneficial when a person is sick, we designate the plant a medicinal plant or herb. Examples would be hop tea to calm the nerves; castor oil to stimulate the colon (producing laxation); and quinine to kill the parasites causing malaria. The effect produced is that of a medicine or drug.

A Botanic Drug and a Regular Drug Defined

In the next few paragraphs we will discuss two entities: a medicinal herb (botanic drug) and a purified active ingredient (regular drug) derived from the medicinal herb. A practitioner of botanic medicine prescribes the first, while regular physicians use the latter. The question is: Is one better than the other?

The active ingredient is the chemical in a plant that makes a particular plant a medicinal herb. It is a "medicine" packaged with hundreds of other chemicals that the plant needs for its own existence. The only reason it is unique is because we believe it to have curative powers, the ability to relieve some illness or disease when consumed by humans.

A medicinal plant may have only one active ingredient or it may have many. Several chemically related compounds or entirely different compounds may be present side by side. And these chemicals may have similar or quite different actions. The foxglove, which we have discussed previously, has a number of glucosides. The molecules are slightly different one from the other. Their actions on a failing heart vary only slightly as does their toxicity. In the regular drug pharmacologists remove and purify the glucoside that is clinically the most active and the least toxic.

Conditions That Affect Medicinal Plants

Soil and other environmental conditions affect herbs and their constituent chemicals. The quality of soil, the degree of moisture available, varying weather conditions (temperature, humidity, cloudy days, etc.), insect pests, the time of harvesting—all may affect the way in which the plant develops and thus determine the amount of the active ingredients present. The method of drying and storing (humidity, temperature, exposure to air) of the medicinal plant also determines how well we preserve the desired botanic drug or drugs (active ingredients). The medicinally active constituents of a plant vary in quantity from plant to plant, and even in the same plant from time to time. These separate but intertwining problems cause the concentration of the active ingredients of herbal preparations to vary widely.

One readily sees how difficult it becomes to determine the dose or the amount of the preparation that we should give to the patient. If the growing season is drier than usual, the active ingredients may have a higher concentration, requiring a smaller dose. Other conditions may lower the average amounts present, necessitating a larger dose. Environmental conditions may also influence the quantities of undesirable or toxic chemicals present in the plant. If, for instance, the concentration of the active ingredient went down but the toxic elements remained the same or increased, giving a larger dose might cause serious problems.

The tomato makes an interesting example. If the weather is cloudy, reducing the intensity of sunlight for a day or two prior to harvesting, the vitamin C present in the fruit may drop to very low levels. But a few days of sunshine will restore the content of vitamin C to normal. Whether tomatoes are staked versus allowed to grow on the ground (thus receiving less light exposure) can alter the amount of vitamin C.[14]

Florida orange juice has less solids in its juice than does corresponding California orange juice. Summer rains and tropical humidity in Florida provide a more moist environment and are in sharp contrast to the low humidity of the rainless summers and near desertlike conditions of California. Ounce for ounce Florida orange juice has less body, or solids, than does California orange juice.

As chemical methods improved, and the sciences of physiology, pharmacology, microbiology, and pathology advanced, researchers made every effort to determine the precise chemical in a medicinal herb that would target a specific disease-producing agent or an afflicted organ. This greatly helped in determining the appropriate dose. Medical science isolated quinine from the bark of the cinchona tree and administered it to destroy the malarial parasite that had invaded the red blood cells. Digoxin, a cardiac glucoside removed from the leaves of the common foxglove, became prescribed for heart failure. Researchers derived salicylic acid and later acetylsalicylic acid (aspirin) from willow bark. The former has served as a treatment for arthritis, while we widely use the latter for headaches, general aches and pains, and thinning the blood. While we could cite countless others, we will look at just one more, a relatively recent example.

Rauwolfia is the crude product derived from the snakeroot. Medical practitioners in India have for centuries employed preparations of snakeroot to calm hyperactive patients. When physicians first introduced rauwolfia into modern medicine they used the powdered root for a short period, but soon replaced it with reserpine, the purified active ingredient. Reserpine has served as a tranquilizer and as an antihypertensive (to lower blood pressure).

We refer to the plant or plant part containing the desired medicinal property as the vegetable drug or botanic drug, while the chemical responsible for the medicinal response is the active ingredient, or pure drug. Today, if we prescribe them as a medicine, we classify both the botanic preparations and the purified products as drugs.

Points to Consider When Using Medicinal Herbs

Dr. Andrew Weil, a graduate of Harvard Medical School, has served in the Department of Integrated Medicine, College of Medicine, University of Arizona. Both a physician and a practitioner of botanic medicine, he has written extensively in the area of alternative medicine. Thus he is able to both support and critique not only regular medicine but also alternative healing methods. "The herb industry is booming today," he comments. "A great deal of its promotional efforts are pure baloney, and unsubstantiated claims are all too common. Just as health food stores display the latest miracle supplements, so do they glamorize miracle herbs."[15]

"In general the herbal products you can buy in stores are not harmful," he observes. "They may be ineffective, but they are more likely to do harm to your pocketbook than to your body. There are a few exceptions."[16] Regarding the effectiveness of herbal products, he is equally forceful in expressing himself. "If toxicity of herbal products is mostly a nonissue, the question of efficacy is a real concern. One reason that regular medicine embraced chemical drugs with such enthusiasm in the last century was that they made possible the administration of exact doses of known compounds. *Herbal medicine can be terribly inexact. How can you be sure that an herbal preparation contains the right plant in the right amount or that it has preserved the desired activity of that plant? . . .*

"Dried plants deteriorate on exposure to air, light, and moisture. Leaves and flowers deteriorate quickly, bark and thick roots more slowly. The more finely chopped the plants' parts are, the faster they lose their desirable qualities. Do not buy whole dried herbs from bins or jars in stores."[17]

As we discussed previously, the variables within herbal preparations pose a significant problem for the user. Dr. Weil has given this as the major reason regular medicine went from using the herbal product to the purified active ingredient. Here are some points that we should always consider.

Some Benefits From Using Purified Active Ingredients

It allows for exact dosage. The dose of a drug is extremely important, and has always been a source of concern. Paracelsus (1493-1541) long ago noted that "all substances are poisons; there is none which is not a poison. The right dose differentiates a poison and a remedy."[18] This is very true. For instance, a small amount of salt (sodium chloride) is essential for life, but large amounts will kill. The same applies to vitamins. Small amounts are necessary for life itself, while large ones will cause illness.

In determining what the dose of an agent (medication) should be, we must keep in mind a number of factors. They include: What is the potency of the agent, measured by its strength to produce physiological effects? What is the concentration of the agent in the herb (medication)? Again, what is the concentration found in the blood or tissues after the patient takes it? How rapidly does the person's body absorb the agent? What concentrations are desirable in the tissues, and how soon can we attain them? How long can we maintain the concentration of the drug at an effective level? How promptly is the drug destroyed by the liver or excreted by the kidneys?

It is precisely for these and other reasons (for example, purified products store better) that pharmacologists extract, purify, and make ready for use the medicinal ingredients of plants. It enables the practitioner to prescribe an exact dose, anticipate the desired response, minimize the possibility of overdosage, control to a large extent adverse reactions, and care for the patient in a more reliable fashion.

Using chemically isolated agents allows medical researchers to observe the precise responses from a given dose and to compare the results with those obtained by other investigators.

It is true that tests are sometimes done on commercially available medicinal herbs to determine as far as possible the concentrations of the active ingredients present in the herb. When using botanic drugs the consumer should check to see if such assays have been made. However, such tests rarely measure other chemicals present, some of them possibly toxic.

It provides additional ways to administer the drug. Purified products lend themselves to be given subcutaneously, intramuscularly, and intravenously, while a crude preparation works only with substances that the body can tolerate when ingested by mouth.

It enables the drug to begin working more quickly. Many conditions, such as certain arrhythmias (irregularities) of the heart, advanced renal failure, infections of the spinal cord, and certain allergic conditions require immediate action, so the response to an herbal preparation would be too slow to be of value. Oftentimes quick action is imperative. Time is of the essence. One cannot wait. We can give many regular drugs by vein, in the muscle, or under the skin. Whether one can inject a drug may be a matter of life or death.

It reduces interaction of medications. The increasing use of botanic drugs by the lay public has created a potentially serious problem. It is well known that regular drugs may interact with one another, resulting in serious toxic reactions. In the same way a botanic drug may interact adversely with another botanic drug. In addition, patients taking regular drugs, for example, for an illness cared for by a physician, may then dose themselves with one or more self-prescribed botanic drugs, often not disclosed to the attending physician. Interactions between the regular drug and the botanic drug may lead to serious consequences. The botanic drug may neutralize the regular drug, or vice versa. The interactions may also produce new chemical combinations that may be toxic. Even if the patient informs the physician as to what herb or herbs he or she is taking, the exact chemical ingredients in a particular botanic drug may be still unknown.

It removes harmful substances. Isolating the active ingredient from a plant avoids any toxic substances that the medicinal herb may also contain. This will then lower the toxicity, making the drug less harmful. For example, removing recin from castor bean oil eliminates a highly toxic substance, allowing us to use the oil therapeutically without dangerous side effects.

Is Herbal Medicine Effective?

The marketing of herbal preparations is a multibillion-dollar-a-year business. The above question is a good one, and the answer, as one might expect, is yes and no. Many botanic drugs do work. If they didn't, medical science would have never discovered many of the regular drugs used by physicians. Such regular drugs were the active ingredients of medicinal herbs prior to their being chemically isolated and purified. Two examples would be ephedrine, found and removed from *Ephedra sinica,* a plant found in the desert Southwest; and reserpine, long used in India, derived from snakeroot *(Rauwolfia serpentina).*

Some believe that medicinal herbs or botanic drugs are less

toxic than their purified active ingredients. They hold that when we take a medicinal herb as found in nature, the beneficial and harmful chemicals balance each other out, so that we will encounter no undesirable side effects. Unfortunately, no evidence supports such a belief. In fact, much evidence points to the contrary. We have already noted one example in the need to purify castor oil. Another case in point would be the use of foxglove for a failing heart. The crude preparation of digitalis (ground leaf or extract) of foxglove will cause more severe nausea, vomiting, cramps, and diarrhea than does its purified active glucoside, digoxin.

The claim that botanic drugs do no harm is, unfortunately, not true. One reason that botanic drugs (herbal preparations) might at first glance appear to be less harmful is that the concentration of the active ingredient is relatively low in most herbal preparations. This is both good and bad. While it produces fewer toxic responses, it may also be completely ineffective. Because of the low concentration of the active principle the drug never reaches threshold concentration required to activate the target cells, so the botanic drug is neither toxic nor beneficial. It may be said, then, that in general a medicinal herb or a botanic drug *is a medicine (drug) in which its active ingredients are in relatively low concentration or in dilute solution.*

However, if the body does not promptly destroy or eliminate the active ingredient, the concentration may gradually over time (days or weeks) accumulate in the body tissues until its concentration finally reaches the threshold level to trigger the desired response. Medical science calls this the *cumulative effect.* Should this be the case, we must reduce the intake of the botanic drug to prevent the active ingredient from building up to toxic levels.

Common Action of Both Botanic Drugs and Regular Drugs

Both botanic drugs and regular drugs may show beneficial effects because of the same active ingredient as well as the ever-present placebo effect (see chapter 12).

Do botanic drugs have advantages over regular drugs? On occasion the answer is yes. The generally lower concentration of the active ingredient decreases the possibility of toxic reactions. Doses that don't reach the threshold level of response sometimes allow the body's own natural resources to recover from the problem even though the medicine is otherwise ineffective. Rapid absorption from the gastrointestinal tract or by injection can cause a drug to reach toxic levels quickly. That is why it is vital to determine the dose carefully. The medical staff must consider the many variables surrounding dosage, so as to give an effective dose and at the same time keep it below the toxic level.

What Botanic Drugs Are Beneficial?

This is, of course, the answer healers have sought down through the ages! If but a fraction of the claims one hears promoted by advertising agencies, or those one can read in a variety of magazines, or find in stores that sell botanic drugs and herbal preparations were true, the question above would have a definite answer. But the very fact that it does not, and that regular medicine is also constantly changing its therapeutic agents, tells us something important. Some well-established herbal agents work for specific problems, but they make up only a few of the hundreds of plant drugs that come and go in the marketplace.

The National Institutes of Health and researchers around the world are actively studying medicinal herbs and food plants to determine whether the various claims made for their therapeutic value have any validity. Some examine herbs for their healing properties, while others determine their chemical constituents. An article in the *American Journal of Clinical Nutrition* has two interesting tables that illustrate a few of the findings.[19]

The reader must understand that the author is not attempting to prescribe specific agents, botanic or regular, but only to help the reader understand Ellen White's counsels and instructions. Anyone desiring to use herbs and herbal preparations will find many books on the subject in libraries and the bookstores.[20]

Cautions Regarding Self-medication

The question of self-medication is an important one. We are all

Active Chemicals Found in Herbs

Herbal source	Active phytochemicals
Allium (garlic, onions, leeks, and chives)	diallyl sulfide, disulfides, and trisulfides
Labiatae family (basil, dill, fennel, marjoram, mint, rosemary, oregano, sage, thyme)	monoterpenes, sesquiterpenes, and flavinoids; rosemary and sage contain diterpenoids (rosmanol, carnosol, carnosic acid, rosmarinic acid, epirosmanol, and isorosmanol), and ursolic acid (triterpenoid)
Umbellifereae family (anise, caraway, coriander, celery seed, cilantro, cumin, dill, fennel, and parsley)	coumarins, phthalides, polyacetylenes, and terpenoids
Zingiberaceae family (turmeric, ginger)	curcumin, gingerols, and diarylheptanoids
green tea	—epigallocatechin gallate and other catechins
licorice	glycyrrhizin (a triterpenoid saponin) and chalcones
flaxseed	lignans
tarragon	terpenoids

Terpenoids Known to Inhibit Tumors

Terpenoid	Herbs that contain the active terpenoid
carvone	caraway, spearmint, and dill
cineole	coriander, lavender, rosemary, sage, and thyme
farnesol	lemongrass, chamomile, and lavender
geraniol	lemongrass, coriander, melissa, basil, and rosemary
lemonene	caraway, mints, cardamom, dill, celery seed, coriander, and fennel
menthol	peppermint
perillyl alcohol	lavender, spearmint, sage
ápinene	caraway, coriander, fennel, juniper berry, rosemary, and thyme

subject to bias. The ever-present placebo effect (discussed in detail in chapter 12) makes it extremely difficult for anyone to evaluate his or her response to a medicine. To be objective with oneself is almost impossible. Hence science uses the double-blind study method. The principal investigators never have contact with the subjects they are studying, lest their personal bias influence the investigation and conclusions. They work through others who do not know the goals of the research.

I remember a personal experience I had one winter many years ago. A bad cold had developed into laryngitis and finally bronchitis. My cough persisted and got worse. Then I began breaking out with giant hives. Sometimes they covered almost my entire body. One night I awoke having difficulty in breathing. When I tried to arouse my wife I could not make a sound. After rolling out of bed and crawling to a nearby bathroom, I groped for a syringe. I had been giving myself shots of adrenaline. Finally—it seemed hours—I found the syringe and injected the adrenaline. A few minutes later I walked to my bedroom and got back into bed.

The next morning I called a physician friend. He checked me over and prescribed some medication. As he was leaving, he paused, looked at me closely, and said, "Mervyn, I want to give you some advice. Whenever a physician treats himself, he has a fool for a patient and a fool for a doctor." I have never forgotten his advice. I trust that you, the reader, will not forget it either.

Points to Consider

A medicinal herb or botanic drug is a plant used as a medicine. The plant tissues contain an active ingredient in low concentration. A regular drug, in this context, is the purified active ingredient extracted from the tissues of the medicinal plant and employed for the same purpose.

Anyone who tries medicinal herbs must realize that there is nothing ethereal or magical about a botanic drug. Whenever someone takes a medicinal herb (for whatever purpose) he or she is consuming a drug or drugs in a milieu of hundreds of other chemicals that form the plant's structure and generate its functions.

Andrew Weil offers the following advice to anyone interested in botanic medicine.[21]

- *"Loose herbs sold in bulk are probably worthless."*
- *"Encapsulated, powdered herbs are also likely to be worthless."*
- *"Herbal products may be contaminated or adulterated."*
- *"Tinctures and freeze-dried extracts of medicinal plants are the best preparations to buy."*
- *"Discontinue use of any herbal product to which you have an adverse reaction."*
- *"Do not take herbal medicines unless you need them."*
- *"Experiment with herbal remedies conscientiously."*

Experimenting on Oneself

I cannot agree with Dr. Weil on his final recommendation—that is, to experiment on yourself with herbal preparations. You, the reader, and I, the author, are humans and find it difficult to be objective. Walter Lewis and Memory Elvin-Lewis have warned us about self-medication: "We recognize that our attraction to self-medication has made us vulnerable to exploitation by those who foster the use of natural substances without reasonable knowledge of their scientific value."[22]

Some may claim that Ellen White encouraged such experimentation, but I do not believe so. She suggested to those having difficulty digesting certain foods to try different foods and combinations of foods (CG 386, MH 295-298, CD 94, 96, 491, 494), but she warned physicians against experimenting with drugs in regard to their patients. Herbal medicines, or vegetable drugs, may contain highly toxic substances. The risk to one's health is far too great than to take needless chances.

And while I'm dispensing advice, I might as well toss out a trifle more! People who are marketing a product almost without exception get excellent results from taking that product!

Summary

A medicinal herb is a plant or plant part that has within its tissues one or more chemicals that someone believes to have healing properties. Such "vegetable drugs" (Webster) or "botanic drugs" are generally in low concentration and, as a result, show less toxicity. When we extract, purify, and concentrate the medical components, they become regular drugs prescribed by physicians.

With this understanding of what comprises both a medicinal herb, or botanic drug, and a regular drug, let us thoughtfully examine the counsels and instructions Ellen White has given on the subject.

SECTION II

Herbs and Ellen White

That Ellen White recommended the use of herbs in cases of illness goes without question. It is interesting, however, that none of her published works mention herbal therapy. Her references to herbs are nowhere as extensive as those on drugs. In contrast they are relatively few. Let us look at some examples:

"God has caused to *grow out of the ground,* herbs for the use of man, and if we understand the nature of these roots and herbs, and make a right use of them, there would not be a necessity of running to the doctor so frequently, and people would be in much better health than they are today" (letter 35, 1890, 2SM 297, 298; italics supplied).

"The Lord has given *some simple herbs of the field* that at times are beneficial. . . . These old-fashioned, simple herbs, used intelligently, would have recovered many sick who have died under drug medication" (letter 82, 1897, *ibid.* 294; italics supplied).

"There are *herbs that are harmless,*[23] the use of which will tide over many apparently serious difficulties" (manuscript 86, 1897, *ibid.* 291; italics supplied).

"This is God's method. The herbs that grow for the benefit of man, and the little handful of herbs kept and steeped for sudden ailments, have served tenfold, yes, one hundred-fold better purpose, than all the drugs hidden under mysterious names and dealt out to the sick" (letter 59, 1898, PC 31; "The Place of Herbs in Rational Therapy" 12).

"The true method for healing the sick is to tell them of the herbs that grow for the benefit of man. Scientists have attached large names to these simplest preparations, but true education will lead us to teach the sick that they need not call in a doctor any more than they would call in a lawyer. They can themselves administer the simple herbs if necessary" (manuscript 105, 1898, SpM 137; "The Place of Herbs in Rational Therapy" 13).

"There are simple herbs that can be used for the recovery of the sick, whose effect upon the system is very different from that of those drugs that poison the blood and endanger life" (manuscript 73, 1908, 2SM 288).

Harmless Herbs—The Physician's Dream

As pointed out earlier in this chapter, medicinal herbs carry in their tissues chemicals that act as medicines or botanic drugs. When isolated, purified, and concentrated, they become the regular drugs of the medical profession. But whether botanic drugs or regular drugs, they are by no means harmless.

The harmless herbs used as medicine that Ellen White mentions are, I believe, food plants.[24] At the time she wrote, scientists had not yet identified vitamins or determined the mineral elements needed by the human body. Pioneering research had shown that whole-grain rice and wheat cured beriberi and pellagra, and lemon juice cured scurvy. Today we know that the human body requires some 50 or more vitamins and minerals, all obtained through our food. A wide spectrum of serious diseases—scurvy, beriberi, pellagra, iron deficiency anemia, hemorrhagic disease of the newborn, goiter, rickets, and night blindness—result from a lack of specific nutrients.

Vitamins and minerals are essential to our health and well-being. They, like the phytochemicals mentioned on page 138, are harmless when consumed in our food. When taken in large amounts, however, they act not as nutrients but as chemicals, a phenomena termed the "drug action of nutrients."

Recent discoveries have revealed hundreds of chemicals in foods that play extremely important biological roles within our bodies. Knowledge regarding these food components is still fragmentary, but we understand that their absence in the diet may result in killer diseases, such as arteriosclerosis, coronary heart disease, and a number of malignancies. Dietary fiber and antioxidant phytochemicals have a crucial part in lowering the risk of, or preventing, such diseases as heart disease and colorectal cancer. Also such substances help control Type II diabetes and appear to enhance the effectiveness of our immune systems.

"Review of the epidemiological data, including both cohort and case-control studies, of all cancer sites strongly suggests that plant foods also have preventive potential and that consumption of the following groups and types of vegetables and fruits is lower in those who subsequently develop cancer: raw and fresh vegetables, leafy green vegetables, cruciferae, carrots, broccoli, cabbage, lettuce, and raw and fresh fruit (including tomatoes and citrus fruit). Other data suggest that foods high in phytoestrogens, particularly soy (which contains isoflavones), or high in precursor compounds that can be metabolized by gut bacteria into active agents, particularly some grains and vegetables with woody stems (which contain precursors to lignans), are plausibly associated with a lower risk of sex-hormone-related cancers. . . .

"There are many biologically plausible reasons why consumption of plant foods might slow or prevent the appearance of cancer. These include the presence in plant foods of such potentially anticarcinogenic substances as carotenoids, vitamin C, vitamin E, selenium, dietary fibre (and its components), dithiolthiones, isothiocyanates, indoles, phenols, protease inhibitors, allium compounds, plant sterols, and limonene. Phytoestrogens are also derived from some vegetables and berries as well as grains and seeds."[25]

Ellen White Grew Fruits and Vegetables

Food distribution systems such as we have today did not exist in Ellen White's time. Local farms and kitchen gardens provided most of the food supply. "April was a busy month for gardening. From the Italian garden nearby they secured a large number of strawberry plants. She and Addie Walling joined Brother Bellow in planting them. A good many grapevines were also set out (letter 8, 1882). A few days later she secured from the Italian garden beet and spinach plants to transplant. Also she helped in planting seeds for parsnips, cabbage, carrots, and beets. 'We shall have quite a garden,' she wrote, 'if the Lord favors us.'"[26]

"We are very pleased to be at home again. Yesterday we gathered peas from our garden for dinner. This is the second dish we have had this season" (letter 14, 1906, 21MR 83).

"Soon after getting settled in the home on Mount Hope Avenue, arrangements were made to have the open land near the house prepared for a spring garden. As the plow started to turn the soil Ellen noticed many small potatoes that had not frozen during the mild winter. The drought the preceding year had resulted in a crop thought not worth harvesting. What a find! Soon Ellen, with pail in hand, was following the plowman, gathering in what she saw to be a precious harvest."[27]

Which Plant Remedies Did Ellen White Recommend?

The question arises as to which plants or herbs and roots Ellen White had in mind in her statements on herbs as medicine. A careful search of all her available writings turns up only a few examples. Those she used herself or recommended as medicine appear in the remedies table in chapter 6, and include catnip, hop, eucalyptus, red clover, and ginger.

The statements below suggest that she had other such agents in her repertoire (armamentarium) of herbal remedies. "There are many more simple remedies which will do much to restore healthful action to the body" (letter 35, 1890, 2SM 297). While "simple remedies" covers a broad field of remedial agents, she made the above statement in the context of advocating the use of medicinal herbs. "There are many simple herbs which, if our nurses would learn the value of, they could use in the place of drugs, and find very effective" (letter 90, 1908, *ibid.* 295).

The following quotation is a rather startling one, as it opens up a rather broad spectrum of herbal remedies. The larger part of medical agents used by the physicians of her day were plants or preparations obtained from plants. The example she gave makes clear that she was referring to herbs.

"The common words by which we know simple remedies *are as useful as the technical terms used by physicians for these same remedies.* To request a nurse to prepare some catnip tea, answers the purpose as well as would directions given to her [by a physician] in language understood only after long study" (manuscript 169, 1902, quoted in 19MR 48; italics supplied).

Clearly Ellen White here recommended herbal remedies that were in use among the medical profession, and that the language physicians employed when prescribing such medicines was Latin. She objected to the custom of concealing their identity from the patient (letter 82, 1897, 2SM 294, 290). Latin was the language used for prescription writing (manuscript 169, 1902 [19MR 38-54]).[28]

How to Distinguish the Good From the Bad

The problem that we now face is how to determine which of the scores of plant remedies in common use by physicians Ellen White did recommend. In her reply to the medical student Edgar Caro she deals, in part, with this problem. She writes: "I do not think that I can give you any definite line of medicines compounded and dealt out by doctors, that are perfectly harmless." And then she adds: "And yet it would not be wisdom to engage in controversy over this subject" (letter 17a, 1893, 2SM 279).

What Can We Conclude?

Ellen White speaks highly of medicinal herbs: "The true method for healing the sick is to tell them of the herbs that grow for the benefit of man" (manuscript 105, 1898, SpM 137). Again: "The Lord has given some simple herbs of the field that at times are beneficial" (letter 82, 1897, 2SM 294). She also indicates that there are many such herbs, and that the physicians use them.

Herbs that are biologically active in humans are almost countless. Which of them did she have in mind—harmless, less harmful, moderately harmful, or poisonous? The purified active ingredients of medicinal herbs (botanic drugs) were gradually becoming available toward the end of Ellen White's ministry. The question we must ask ourselves is: Would she have used one in preference to the other?

The following chapter presents medicinal herbs, both "harmless" and "harmful," in the context of simple remedies as a whole. It will provide an understanding of these terms and will hopefully aid in differentiating the acceptable from the nonacceptable.

References

[1] This chapter seeks to provide sufficient information regarding regular drugs and botanic drugs so that the reader can better understand the subject of medicinal herbs. Readers should not, however, attempt to use it to diagnose or treat their maladies or those of others.

[2] Walter H. Lewis and P. F. Memory Elvin-Lewis, *Medical Botany* (New York: John Wiley & Sons, 1977), p. 8.

[3] The plant's chemicals function in the plant, but God did not intend them for general human use as food or drink.

[4] A. S. Lyons and R. J. Petrucelli, *Medicine: An Illustrated History*, pp. 105-119; C. Norman Shealy, *The Illustrated Encyclopedia of Healing Remedies* (Boston: Element Books Inc., 1998), pp. 18-23.

[5] Lyons and Petrucelli, pp. 121, 124; Shealy, p. 49.

[6] Lyons and Petrucelli, p. 77.

[7] *Ibid.*, pp. 59, 63, 67.

[8] *Ibid.*, pp. 153, 185, 186, 207-210, 219.

[9] *Ibid.*, pp. 254, 258, 259.

[10] R. H. Shryock, *Medicine in America*, pp. 123, 229, 230; Rothstein, *American Physicians*, p. 62.

[11] *Merriam-Webster's Collegiate Dictionary*, 10th ed.

[12] *The Dispensatory of the United States of America*, 20th ed. (Philadelphia: J. B. Lippincott Co., 1918), pp. 1648, 286-289, 403-409, 338-352, 803-820, 512-576, 270-275; Lucius E. Sayre, *A Manual of Organic Materia Medica and Pharmacognosy*, 3rd ed., revised by William C. Stevens (Philadelphia: P. Blakiston's Son & Co., 1906), pp. 340, 341, 393, 342-344, 261-268, 107-109, 81-84, 382-384.

[13] *Webster's Ninth New Collegiate Dictionary*.

[14] Karl C. Hamner, Leon Bernstein, and L. A. Maynard, "Effects of Light Intensity, Day Length, Temperature, and Other Environmental Factors on the Ascorbic Acid Content of Tomatoes," *Journal of Nutrition* 29 (January-June 1945): 85-97.

[15] Andrew Weil, "Natural Health, Natural Medicine," in *The Herbal Medicine Chest* (Boston: Houghton-Mifflin Co., 1990), p. 230.

[16] *Ibid.*

[17] *Ibid.*, p. 232. (Italics supplied.)

[18] Quoted in "Principles of Toxicology and Treatment of Poisoning," in Goodman and Gilman, *The Pharmacological Basis of Therapeutics*, p. 64.

[19] Winston J. Craig, *American Journal of Clinical Nutrition* 70 (suppl.) (1999): 495S.

[20] One example is Winston Craig's *The Use and Safety of Common Herbs and Herbal Teas* (Golden Harvest Books, 4610 Lisa Lane, Berrien Springs, Michigan

49103). I am in no way endorsing Dr. Craig's philosophies, but for anyone contemplating their use, it may answer some of the reader's concerns and provide cautions.

[21] Weil, pp. 232, 233.

[22] Lewis and Elvin-Lewis, p. viii.

[23] Most probably God was instructing Ellen White that health-producing substances were present in herbs or food plants (Gen. 3:18). When the Lord told Adam that he was to eat the "herb of the field" "all the days of thy life" (verse 19) it is doubtful that He meant that medicinal plants should be a staple diet.

[24] See chapter 7.

[25] J. D. Potter and K. Steinmetz, "Vegetables, Fruit and Phytoestrogens as Preventive Agents," *International Agency for Research on Cancer Scientific Publishing* 139 (1996): 61-90.

[26] Letter 8, 1882, quoted in Arthur L. White, *Ellen G. White: The Lonely Years 1876-1891* (Washington, D.C.: Review and Herald Pub. Assn., 1984), vol. 3, p. 195.

[27] Arthur L. White, *Ellen G. White: The Early Years 1827-1862* (Washington, D.C.: Review and Herald Pub. Assn., 1985), vol. 1, pp. 271, 272.

[28] I still remember how relieved my medical class was to learn that we no longer had to know Latin to write prescriptions.

CHAPTER NINE

A Physician Explains . . .

SIMPLE REMEDIES

SECTION I

A remedy is, according to Webster, "that which relieves or cures a disease; any medicine or application which puts an end to disease and restores health."[1] Such a definition would include a wide range of types and systems of healing: Ayurvedic medicine of India, Chinese medicine, allopathy (regular medicine), homeopathy, osteopathy, naturopathy, alternative medicine, and others, each providing its own particular agents and procedures.

In our discussion we will limit our attention to those areas that deal with Ellen White's counsels on therapeutic agents and procedures, and only allude to other systems when such a reference would provide for a better understanding of the subject.

What Is a Simple Remedy?

I had always assumed that a simple remedy was any measure employed in the treatment of an illness or disease that was easy to give, acted physiologically, and would cause no harm. As I studied the subject more deeply I discovered the phrase "simple remedy," at the time Ellen White used it in her writings, had a much wider meaning. Here is what I found.

"Simple" used as an adjective. A remedy is, as mentioned already, any procedure, application, or medicine that will relieve or cure an illness or disease. A simple remedy is a remedy that is simple. Here we use the word "simple" as an adjective, referring to something that is not complex and is easy to understand and apply.

The adjective "simple" is "single; uncompounded; uncombined; not blended with something else; elementary; as, a *simple* substance, color, or medicinal preparation."[2] You will notice that one meaning given under "simple" is a medicinal preparation. "Simple" here acts as an adjective to designate a single medicine as opposed to a mixture (two or more agents in a single preparation). Thus "simple" and "single" are synonyms.

"Simple" used as a noun. Looking for the meaning of "simple" as a noun, we find that Webster defines the word quite explicitly: "A medicinal herb or medicine obtained from a herb: so called because each vegetable was supposed to possess its particular virtue and, therefore, to constitute a simple remedy."[3] Here Webster makes clear that each medicinal herb, extract, or active ingredient obtained from the herb constitutes a simple remedy.

According to the *Oxford English Dictionary* the phrase "simple remedy" to refer to a medicinal herb was primarily in use from the fifteenth to eighteenth centuries. Although the word "drug" gradually replaced "simple remedy," it lingered into the twentieth century (see, for example, Joseph Meyer's reference to herbal teas as simples in his *The Herbalist and Herb Doctor* [Hammond, Ind.: Indiana Botanic Garden, 1918]).

From the fifteenth century to the early nineteenth century pharmacopeias and books on Materia Medica commonly classified medicines or drugs under the headings of "Singles," "Simples," and "Mixtures." Over time the distinguishing terms disappeared, and by the late nineteenth century any agent or preparation employed as a medicine, whether it contained one or more ingredients, became known by the common word "drug."

An interesting account of how Ellen White's time used the word "simples" appears in a book written by a physician named W. T. Fernie. Entitled *Meals Medicinal: With "Herbal Simples,"* it came off the press in England in 1905.[4] The preface recounts a story about Sir Walter Scott's encounter with a country doctor and the medicines he used to treat his patients. "It is told that Sir Walter Scott, having occasion to seek medical aid unexpectedly in a small country town, found a doctor there, one John Lundie, a grave, sagacious-looking man, attired in black, with a shovel hat, who said, 'My practice is vera sure: I depend entirely upon twa simples.' 'And what may they be?' asked Sir Walter. 'My twa simples,' replied John, in a low confidential tone, 'are just laudamy[5] and calamy.'[6] 'Simples with a vengeance!' quoth Scott; 'And how about your patients, John?' 'Whiles they dies; whiles no,' answered he, 'but it's the will o' Providence.' "

The Fernie then comments: "Our assumption, today, is that (in lieu of drugs) an adequate sufficiency of component curative parts stands similarly within most of our ordinary dishes and drinks if judiciously appointed and skillfully applied. It rests with the enlightened physician, and the well-informed housewife, to make themselves practically acquainted with these principles for cure, as possessed by foods and beverages which can be specially prepared and prescribed for the several maladies as they come under management. In which respect we likewise in our case advocate a practice of treating the sick and the ailing, chiefly with 'twa simples,' representative of leading kinds, to wit the Cabbage and the Egg. These are our laudamy and calamy of today, our compendiums of restorative, sedative, and alterative powers and virtues."

Dr. Fernie's "laudamy" and "calamy"

While the doctor believed that food plays an important role in curing illness and disease, he advocated foods and beverages of every stripe and variety. We will mention a few examples from each class. They included foods of animal origin—beef, brain, bacon, chicken, fish, eel, frogs, rat, dog, milk, cheese, eggs, wasp sting, and snail; foods of plant origin (including the main portions of his herbal simples)—grains, fruits, berries, vegetables, nuts; medicinal herbs—tobacco, snuff, goosegrass, elderberry, seaweeds, hops, catnip, willow, whortleberry, tea, coffee, turpentine, and toadflax; beverages—alcohol, whisky, gin, rum, wine, and beer. Each in some form or other he believed had curative powers.

It is of considerable interest, as we will discuss later, that Dr. Fernie included in his "simples" medicinal herbs, of which he mentions a few, including hops, catnip, tea, and coffee. Among his beverages he recommends alcohol in various forms.

The Cottage Physician, prepared by "the best physicians and surgeons of modern practice, and published in 1896, discussed, under the heading of "Diseases and Their Remedies," various illnesses according to their symptoms, causes, and treatment. The book was designed "for individual and family use." The section on the inflammation of the larynx (laryngitis) further illustrates our point. After describing the problem and the symptoms, the physicians prescribe the following:

"Treatment—In the treatment of this disease, active remedies should be used promptly. If a *blister* is applied, it should be on the upper part of the sternum or chest, rather than on the front of the throat. The compound *syrup of squills* in one-quarter of a teaspoon dose may afford relief. *Calomel* in five grain doses should be given to stimulate glandular secretion. *Purgatives* should also be administered, and warm *fomentations* applied to the throat. A *poultice* made of fine cut tobacco, or tobacco ointment, will often afford relief. As the danger of this disease lies in its tendency to produce suffocation, whenever there is great danger of this termination, *tracheotomy* should be performed, and an artificial opening made, through which the operation of breathing may be carried on till the parts of the larynx acquire their natural state. Nor should this operation be too long delayed. When simple remedies do not afford relief consult your physician without delay."[7]

While I'm sure the doctors did not include a tracheotomy among their "simple remedies," the reader must be relieved that the treatment of laryngitis today does not include all of the above "simple remedies"—syrup of squills, calomel, and purgatives. The poultice of tobacco leaves and fomentations to the throat are without doubt the best of the suggested treatments.

The reader will recall that in Edgar Caro's letter to Ellen White, when he inquired as to her classification of drugs and "simpler remedies," he gave squills as an example of simpler remedies. *The Cottage Physician* above also considered squills as a simple remedy. It seems quite clear that a simple remedy at the time of Ellen White's writing did include medicinal herbs (botanic drugs) or products derived from them. Three examples of such herbs or medicinal plants (botanic drugs) used as medicines are foxglove, tea leaves, and ephedra.

The common foxglove, *(Digitalis purpurea)*, is "an ornamental European perennial or biennial. . . . Its leaves yield the important drug digitalis."[8]

Notice that Webster calls the active ingredient obtained from this medicinal herb a drug. As I have mentioned previously, when I was a medical student we used digitalis (powdered leaves) or digitalis extract (an extract made from the leaves) for heart failure. Although we assayed the preparations, whether powder or extract, it was difficult to regulate dosage. We prescribed them as drugs. The squills were used for the same purpose and contain virtually the same glucosides.

Today chemists have isolated and purified from the common foxglove and other similar species the specific glucoside compounds that act on the heart. Digoxin (Lanoxin) is the most widely used. The purified glucoside causes less irritation to the gastrointestinal tract, and the medical staff can monitor the dosage more precisely. Medical science still dispenses them as drugs.

Now let us consider some additional herbal simples. One of them is tea,[9] "an aromatic beverage prepared from tea leaves by infusion of boiling water, and taken hot or cold. It has stimulant and tonic properties, due to the alkaloid caffeine, and from the presence of tannin is also strongly astringent."[10]

People around the world use tea, coffee, maté, guarana, and yoco as beverages for their stimulant properties. Caffeine is the chemical agent possessing the stimulating action, and physicians use it in purified form as a drug (medicine). Theophylline, also extracted from tea, serves as bronchial dilator in the treatment of asthma. Tannin in tea was used as an astringent and was also employed to calm the stomach (carminative).

Another simple is ephedra, "a large family of jointed, nearly leafless desert shrubs." It yields the alkaloid ephedrine, known also as mahuang.[11]

Chinese and Japanese medicine has long employed the medicinal herb to treat a variety of problems. People in the United States have used it since the 1880s under the names (caynote, canutilo, whorehouse tea, Mormon tea) for gonorrhea, to dilate the pupils, and aid in bronchial asthma.[12] It has actions similar to adrenaline, and herbal preparations sometimes employ it as a stimulant.

Thus late nineteenth-century medicine classified foxglove and its active ingredient digoxin, tea and its active ingredients caffeine and theophylline, and ephedra with the active ingredient ephedrine as simpler or simple remedies. To them we could add a long list of additional medicinal herbs, each containing one or more active components.[13]

When people during Ellen White's time used "simple" as "single," they had in mind a single medicinal herb or botanic drug, not a mixture. A simple remedy is a medicinal herb (botanic drug) or a product or preparation derived from a medicinal herb.

SECTION II

Ellen White's Use of "Simple Remedy"

The question that we should now consider is, How did Ellen White herself employ "simple remedy"? Did she have in mind— as we generally assume—an uncomplicated, easy to apply, and harmless remedy? Or did she use the phrase to designate medicinal herbs and preparations made from them?

Ellen White's Use of "Simple" as an Adjective

Ellen White encouraged people to keep well, and when ill, to do for themselves what they could, using natural and simple remedies. Notice how she employs the terms *remedy* and *simple:*

"Take warm footbaths into which have been put the leaves from the eucalyptus tree. There is great virtue in these leaves, and if you will try this, you will prove my words to be true. The oil of the eucalyptus is especially beneficial in cases of cough and pains in the chest and lungs. I want you to make a trial of this remedy which is so simple, and which costs you nothing" (letter 20, 1909, 2SM 301).

"I have already told you the remedy I use when suffering from difficulties with my throat. I take a glass of boiled honey, and into this I put a few drops of eucalyptus oil, stirring it in well. When the cough comes on, I take a teaspoonful of this mixture, and relief comes almost immediately. I have always used this with the best of results. I ask you to use the same remedy when you are troubled with the cough. This prescription may seem so simple that you feel no confidence in it, but I have tried it for a number of years and can highly recommend it" *(ibid.)*

"One of the most beneficial remedies is pulverized charcoal, placed in a bag and used in fomentations. This is a most successful remedy. If wet in smartweed boiled, it is still better. I have ordered this in cases where the sick were suffering great pain. . . . The patient slept, the turning point came, and recovery was the result. To students when injured with bruised hands and suffering with inflammation, I have prescribed this simple remedy, with perfect success. The poison of inflammation was overcome, the pain removed, and healing went on rapidly. . . . The simplest remedies may assist nature, and leave no baleful effects after their use" (letter 82, 1897, *ibid.* 294).

"Invalids too often deprive themselves of sunlight. This is one of nature's most healing agents. It is a very simple, therefore not a fashionable remedy, to enjoy the rays of God's sunlight and beautify our homes with its presence" (Testimony 19, 1870, 2T 527).

In these examples Ellen White employs the word "simple" as an adjective, pointing out that there are many remedies that are simple, that is, not complicated, and that are easy to use.

Ellen White and "Simple Remedy" as a Noun

As defined earlier by Webster, a simple remedy is a medicinal herb or a medicine obtained from an herb. In a letter to an overseas church employee, Ellen White describes in some detail the responsibilities a person has to keep well and mentions a number of things that should and should not be done. She then advises what a person should do when he or she has ignored health principles and illness results.

"When I violate the laws God has established in my being, I am to repent and reform, and place myself in the most favorable condition under the doctors God has provided—pure air, pure water, and the healing, precious sunlight.

"Water can be used in many ways to relieve suffering. Drafts of clear, hot water taken before eating (half a quart, more or less), will never do any harm, but will rather be productive of good.

"A cup of tea made from catnip herb will quiet the nerves.

"Hop tea will induce sleep. Hop poultices over the stomach will relieve pain.

"If the eyes are weak, if there is pain in the eyes, or inflammation, soft flannel cloths wet in hot water and salt, will bring relief quickly.

"When the head is congested, if the feet and limbs are put in a bath with a little mustard, relief will be obtained" (letter 35, 1890, 2SM 297).

Let us examine the agents she suggested in her letter. They fall into two groups: 1. Natural remedies—pure air, pure water, and sunlight, three of the eight natural remedies we discussed earlier. 2. Simple remedies. Two are medicinal herbs or botanic drugs, and two are hydrotherapeutic procedures: a hot compress of salt and water, and a half-bath with hot water and with added mustard.

She then continued as to what the Lord expects us to do when we suffer pain and illness: "There are *many more simple remedies* which will do much to restore healthful action to the body. All these *simple preparations* the Lord expects us to use for ourselves, but man's extremities are God's opportunities. If we neglect to do that which is within the reach of nearly every family, and ask the Lord to relieve pain when we are too indolent to make use of these remedies within our power, it is simply presumption" (*ibid.*; italics supplied).

A Further Understanding of Simple Remedies

I would suggest that the reader once again turn to pages 69-74 and reread Ellen White's answer to Edgar Caro's inquiry as to what she considered drugs and what she regarded as "simpler remedies." She accepted both of Caro's classifications. "Potassium, iodine, squills, etc." is the class of agents she defined as "less harmful," contrasting them with "drugs," that is, harsh and poisonous remedies.

Such "simpler remedies"[14] are not completely harmless, however, and she adds that they "are often used when not at all necessary." Just what remedies did she have in mind? The following statement illustrates what she included under the heading "simple remedies." "The common words by which we know simple remedies *are as useful as the technical terms used by physicians for these same remedies.* To request a nurse to prepare some catnip tea, answers the purpose fully as well as would directions given her [by a physician] in language understood only after long study" (manuscript 169, 1902, 19MR 48; italics supplied).

Clearly Ellen White was recommending remedies already in use among the medical profession, medicines that physicians liked to refer to by their Latin names.

As she closed her response to Edgar Caro she wisely added, "And yet it would not be wisdom to engage in controversy over this subject." That controversy did exist and still exists is unfortunately true even as I write these words.

Are "Natural Remedies" and "Simple Remedies" Synonymous?

In brief, Ellen White employed "natural remedies" to describe eight principles of life, then referred to them as "the true remedies." Note the following: "Pure air, sunlight, abstemiousness, rest, exercise, proper diet, the use of water, trust in divine power—these are the true remedies" (MH 127). She also included under natural remedies "the life-giving properties of nature's great medicinal resources"—flowers, trees, bird songs, "the balsam of the pine," and "the fragrance of the cedar and the fir" (MM 231; MH 264). (For a full discussion of natural remedies, see chapter 7.)

In one statement she also called a simple remedy a natural remedy. When referring to the poultice of figs applied to King Hezekiah's boil, Ellen White described it as a "natural remedy." "He [the Lord] told him [the king] to apply a bunch of figs to his sore, and that *natural remedy*, blessed by God, healed him" (letter 82, 1899, 2SM 287). On two other occasions she had both terms in the same statement, making them appear synonymous. When the Saviour healed the blind man, He applied clay to his eyes and told him to wash it off. He did and returned seeing (John 9:7). "The cure could be wrought only by the power of the Great Healer," Ellen White commented, "yet Christ made use of the simple agencies of nature. While He did not give countenance to drug medication, He sanctioned the use of *simple and natural remedies*" (DA 824). Again she used both expressions in an account of how she treated her seriously ill children. "We applied water in various ways, praying the Lord to accept our efforts and give us strength and wisdom to use (not drug medication) but the simple, natural remedies God had provided" (letter 17, 1892, 19MR 227). The latter two references, while mentioning simple and natural together, leave it open as to whether she used the phrases as synonyms.

Speaking of simple remedies, she defines two groups of agents:

1. Medicinal agents, generally plants or herbs, or their products. Fortunately, Ellen White gives a number of examples. She suggests the use of herbs in general, and herbal preparations in particular, such as catnip tea, hop tea (letter 35, 1890, 2SM 297); red clover tea (letter 12, 1888, *ibid.* 302); eucalyptus oil in honey (letter 348, 1908; letter 20, 1908, *ibid.* 300, 301); charcoal water (letter 182, 1899, *ibid.* 299); and in the case of severe illness [nausea], weak regular tea (manuscript 3, 1888, *ibid.* 301, 302); and "genuine" (very strong) coffee (letter 20, 1882, *ibid.* 302, 303).

2. Easily administered therapeutic procedures. Examples include fomentations wet in boiled smartweed (letter 82, 1899, *ibid.* 294); charcoal poultices (letter 90, 1908, *ibid.* 295); a hot foot bath with a little mustard (letter 35, 1890, *ibid.* 297); a compress made with hot water and salt *(ibid.)*; and a poultice made from pulverized charcoal with flaxseed (manuscript 68, 1899, *ibid.* 300).

Ellen White specifically mentioned only a limited number of simple remedies, whether medicinal or procedural. However, she alluded to the existence of a large class of such agents. Here are two such references:

"There are many simple herbs which, if our nurses would

learn the value of, they could use in the place of drugs, and find very effective" (letter 90, 1908, *ibid.* 295).

"God has caused to grow out of the ground, herbs for the use of man, and if we understand the nature of those roots and herbs, and make a right use of them, there would not be a necessity of running for the doctor so frequently, and people would be in much better health than they are today" (letter 35, 1890, *ibid.* 297, 298).

Ellen White further divides medicinal herbs into two groups:

A. Harmless: "There are herbs that are harmless, the use of which will tide over many apparently serious difficulties" (manuscript 86, 1897, *ibid.* 291).

B. Less harmful: "The simpler remedies are less harmful in proportion to their simplicity; but in very many cases these are used when not at all necessary" (letter 17a, 1893, *ibid.* 279; discussed in detail in chapter 8).

The "less harmful" group consists of herbs or their products containing biologically active constituents that we can use as medicine. Since the body does not normally contain such biochemicals, they may produce some undesirable effects.

Summary:

Here, in brief, is how Ellen White used "simple remedy":

1. As an adjective, it stood for a noncomplex, easy-to-use, and safe remedy that might be either a harmless food or herb or a simple procedure.

2. As a noun, it stood for a botanic drug (medicinal herb) that was less harmful than the traditional drugs of the time. Notice the following, already quoted: "The common words by which we know simple remedies *are as useful as the technical terms used by physicians for these same remedies*" (manuscript 169, 1902, 19MR 48; italics supplied).

A further understanding of the phrase "simple remedies" will become clearer in the following chapter, in which we will classify and discuss the various remedies Ellen White used herself or advocated to others.

References

[1] *Webster's New International Dictionary,* 2nd ed.

[2] *Ibid.*

[3] *Webster's New Twentieth-Century Dictionary* (Springfield, Mass.: G. & C. Merriam Co., 1979).

[4] W. T. Fernie, *Meals Medicinal With "Herbal Simples"* (Bristol: John Wright & Co.; London: Simkin, Marshall; Hamilton, Kent & Co., Ltd., 1905), pp. vii, viii.

[5] Laudanum, a tincture of opium containing morphine and codeine.

[6] A fluid extract made from the root of *Acorus calamus,* it has a pungent, aromatic taste. People used it to relieve pain or uneasiness of the stomach and bowels.

[7] *The Cottage Physician* (Springfield, Mass.: King-Richardson Pub. Co., 1896), pp. 197, 198; italics supplied.

[8] *Webster's New International Dictionary,* 2nd ed.

[9] *Thea sinensis.*

[10] *Webster's New International Dictionary,* 2nd ed.

[11] *Ibid.*

[12] W. H. Lewis and P. F. Memory Elvin-Lewis, *Medical Botany,* p. 389; *The Dispensatory of the United States of America,* 20th ed., p. 1373.

[13] See *The Dispensatory.*

[14] Ellen White employed "simpler remedies" on one other occasion. Advising physicians about their broader responsibilities, she said, "The minister will often be called upon to act the part of a physician. He should have a training that will enable him to administer the simpler remedies for the relief of suffering. Ministers and Bible workers should prepare themselves for this line of work, for in doing it they are following the example of Christ. They should be as well prepared by education and practice to combat disease of the body as they are to heal the sin-sick soul by pointing to the Great Physician" (MM 253). Medical licensing laws were not as strict then as they are now.

CHAPTER TEN

A Physician Explains . . .

REMEDIES USED BY ELLEN WHITE

S ome believe that when we become sick we should ask God to heal our illness, and if our faith is strong enough, He will restore our health. Without doubt on occasions this has occurred. If it were true at all times, as Christian Science teaches, it would greatly reduce the number of medical practitioners of every stripe. What did Ellen White believe on this issue? What did she teach? And most important of all, what did she do herself?

Ellen White's Personal Philosophy on Sickness and Therapy

"In regard to that which we can do for ourselves, there is a point that requires careful, thoughtful consideration. I must become acquainted with myself, I must be a learner always as to how to take care of this building, the body God has given me, that I may preserve it in the very best condition of health." She then goes on to say that we should eat wholesome food, dress appropriately, and not deprive ourselves of exercise and fresh air.

"And when I violate the laws God has established in my being, I am to repent and reform, and place myself in the most favorable condition under the doctors God has provided—pure air, pure water, and the healing, precious sunlight." Ellen White specifies a number of remedies that might be of help: water used in many ways to relieve suffering (hydrotherapy); water drunk freely; a cup of catnip tea when nervous, or a cup of hop tea when sleep fails to come; and a foot bath for a congested head.

"There are many more simple remedies which will do much

to restore healthful action to the body. *All these simple preparations the Lord expects us to use for ourselves,* but man's extremities are God's opportunities." Finally, she warns: *"If we neglect to do that which is within the reach of nearly every family, and ask the Lord to relieve pain when we are too indolent to make use of these remedies within our power, it is simply presumption"* (letter 35, 1890, 2SM 296-298; italics supplied).

As we have seen in chapter 6, a careful analysis of Ellen White's writings suggests that she divided remedies (medicines and procedures) into three major groups: (1) natural remedies, (2) simple remedies, and (3) drugs and mixtures.

The remedies that Ellen White either employed herself or recommended to others appear in the tables below and have been placed in one or another of the above categories. Please note that I have given each remedy its most appropriate classification. In some instances it is a judgment call, one that the reader may disagree with.

Remedies Ellen White Used or Recommended		
Simple Remedies		
Medicinal herbs or botanic drugs		
1. Harmless		
Agent	*Active ingredient*	*Uses*[1]
whole foods	many	many preventive and curative
EGW: "In grains, fruits, vegetables, and nuts are to be found all the food elements that we need" (MM 267). Encouraging the consumption of vegetables from the garden and fruit from the orchard, she also used herbs from the field: "As far as material for greens is concerned, you need have no concern; for to my certain knowledge there are in the section of country where you live many kinds of vegetable productions which I can use as greens. I shall be able to obtain the leaves of the yellow dock, the young dandelion, and mustard" (CD 323). "My thistle greens, nicely cooked, and seasoned with sterilized cream and lemon juice, are very appetizing" *(ibid.).*		

charcoal, pulverized	carbon	enteritis (inflammation of the bowels)

EGW: "This man who was suffering from inflammation of the bowels, sent for me to come to him. My husband and I decided that it would not do to move him. Fears were entertained that mortification had set in. Then the thought came to me like a communication from the Lord to take pulverized charcoal, put water upon it, and give this water to the sick man to drink, putting bandages of the charcoal over the bowels and stomach. . . . The result was that in half an hour there was a change for the better. . . . The blessing of God worked with the simple means used" (2SM 299).

charcoal and olive oil (*Olea europaea*)	fixed oil	carminative, laxative

EGW: "I will tell you a little about my experience with charcoal as a remedy. For some forms of indigestion, it is more efficacious than drugs. A little olive oil into which some of this powder has been stirred, tends to cleanse and heal" (*The Place of Herbs in Rational Therapy*, pp. 24, 25).

peppermint (*Mentha piperita*)	volatile oil	nausea, colic, flatus

W. C. White: "The porter brought some hot water. Into this Miss McEnterfer put a little peppermint, and with much difficulty got Mrs. White to swallow a few spoonfuls. Then she vigorously rubbed her hands and arms and feet" (RH Jan. 20, 1910).

2. Less harmful

Agent	*Active ingredient*	*Uses*
ginger, fluid extract or powder—resin (*Zingiberaceae officinale*)	volatile oil	carminative, indigestion, gastritis, colic, diarrhea

EGW: "We have just finished breakfast. It is now five minutes past eight o'clock. We are about ten miles from Laramie. We shall not be able to make way with our provisions. Sara bought a bottle of milk and some warm water this morning. I put ginger in it and it went well" (11MR 70).

EGW: "In regard to our using spice, I plead not guilty. We have not had spice in our house for ten years, except a little ginger, which we have always used to some extent" (15MR 245).

hops, infusion or tea (*Humulus lupulus*)	lupulin	as a bitter (for atonic dyspepsia), hysteria, mild sedative, hypnotic (for insomnia)
EGW: "Hop tea will induce sleep" (2SM 297).		
Catnip, infusion or tea (*Nepta cataria*)	volatile oil, tannin	mild sedative
EGW: "A cup of tea made from catnip herb will quiet the nerves" (*ibid.*).		
eucalyptus oil and honey (especially *Eucalyptus globus*)	oil, volatile oil	antiseptic, infections of upper respiratory tract, cough
EGW: "I cannot advise any remedy for her cough better than eucalyptus and honey. Into a tumbler of honey put a few drops of the eucalyptus, stir it up well, and take whenever the cough comes on" (2SM 300). Also used for sore throat (2SM 301).		
pepper, black (*Piper nigrum*)	resin and volatile oil	flatulence, colic, carminative
EGW: "I have not had, to my knowledge, a particle of pepper in the house for ten years. When Lucinda went up to Mr. Walling's mills, I said to her, 'Get me a little pinch of pepper, and I will try to eat some beans.' I thought the pepper would perhaps prevent them from causing me to have the colic. But I think so little of what I eat, it never entered my mind that there was any pepper. So much for pepper. I claim that we live very plain and economical" (15MR 246).		

PROCEDURES

1. Hydrotherapy		
Agent	*Active ingredient*	*Uses*
fomentations, hot	moist heat to skin	fever, tepid bath
EGW: "Hot fomentations in fever will kill the inflammation in nine cases out of ten where ice applications will, according to the light given me, tax the vitality unsafely. Here is where the danger comes in of not using judgment and reason in regard to the subject under treatment" (letter 189, 1897, quoted in Arthur White, *Ellen G. White: The Australian Years 1891-1900*, vol. 4, 293).		

water, hot with salt	moist heat	inflammation pain (eyes)

EGW: "If the eyes are weak, if there is pain in the eyes, or inflammation, soft flannel cloths wet in hot water and salt, will bring relief quickly" (2SM 297).

smartweed, a tincture *(Polygonum hydropiper)*	polygonic acid	rubefacient (causing redness and warmth to the skin), detergent (in chronic ulcer), in diarrhea, dysentery, uterine disorders

EGW: "Pulverized charcoal, placed in a bag and used in fomentations. This is a most successful remedy. If wet in smartweed boiled, it is still better" (2SM 294).

mustard bath *(Brassia nigra)*	fatty oil, volatile oil	rubefacient

EGW: "When the head is congested, if the feet and limbs are put in a bath with a little mustard, relief will be obtained" (2SM 297).

2. Electrotherapy

Agent	Active ingredient	Uses
electricity (electric battery —6 volt?)	heat, shock	lumbago (pain in low back and thigh)

EGW: "Our electric battery, which has been out of repair, is now in working order; and what relief it brings in sickness! Just as the prunes were ready to pick, Brother James was seized with an attack of what he calls lumbago. He had severe pains in his back, and could neither stand straight, nor bend down far enough to unlace his shoes. Sara gave him electricity, Sister James helping where she could. . . . At first Brother James could hardly endure the application of the electricity, but Sara persevered, and wonderful relief came to him. He now thinks that electricity is a marvelous remedy. After the first application, he was able to walk straighter than he had been able to for days, and he continued to improve. Sara has given him electricity three times a day, and he has been able to keep at his work" (7MR 118).

electricity	shock	uses not known

EGW: "The strongest electricity was employed; one stood with a cake of ice and another with a hot sponge and passed first hot, then cold, over the spine for three hours until my pulse, though very weak, and fluttery, was improved. For four nights these faithful hands battled with death and were rewarded by seeing a determined improvement" (letter 9, 1881, quoted in Arthur White, *Ellen G. White: The Lonely Years 1876-1891*, vol. 3, 180).

EGW: "When we were at the Paradise Valley Sanitarium, we were conducted through the new treatment rooms. One room was elaborately fitted up with electrical appliances for giving patients treatment. That night I was instructed that some connected with the institution were introducing things for the treatment of the sick that were not safe. The application of these electrical treatments would involve the patient in serious difficulties, imperiling life" (*Testimonies and Experiences Connected With the Loma Linda Sanitarium and College of Medical Evangelists* 18).

X-ray	gamma rays	cancer (melanoma)

EGW: "For several weeks I took treatment with the X-ray for the black spot that was on my forehead. In all I took twenty-three treatments, and these succeeded in entirely removing the mark. For this I am very grateful" (2SM 303).

3. Preparations

Agent	Active ingredient	Uses
charcoal (*Carbo ligni*)	carbon	cholic, diarrhea, ulcers, pain

EGW: "Get some pulverized charcoal; make a poultice of it, and lay it over her stomach and sides" (2SM 295).

flaxseed (linseed) (*Linum usitatissimum*)	cake (crushed)	demulcent, poultice

EGW: "Pulverized charcoal, mixed with flaxseed, was placed upon the swelling, and this poultice gave relief at once" (2SM 300).

DRUGS AND MIXTURES

1. Drugs

Agent	Active ingredient	Uses
tea (*Thea sinensis*) used as an infusion	caffeine, theophylline, tannic acid	astringent, carminative (for nausea, vomiting)

EGW: "Once when crossing the waters I was sick and could retain nothing on my stomach and I did take a little weak tea as a medicine" (2SM 301).

EGW: "I have not bought a penny's worth of tea for years. Knowing its influence I would not dare to use it, except in cases of severe vomiting when I take it as a medicine, but not as a beverage" (2SM 302).

coffee (*Coffee arabica*)	caffeine	excitant (for congestive headache), carminative (for vomiting, seasickness)
EGW: "I have not knowingly drunk a cup of genuine coffee for twenty years, only, as I stated, during my sickness—for a medicine—I drank a cup of coffee, very strong, with a raw egg broken into it" (2SM 302, 303).		
wine (fermented)	alcohol	tonic, calming agent?
EGW: "I have not tested the wine that you claim is not intoxicating. I have perhaps used half a pint in all, taking a spoonful with a raw egg, much as I hate the taste of wine. I would not care, even if I had not solemnly pledged myself not to use wine as a beverage, to make a daily practice of taking even one teaspoonful with a raw egg" (*Testimonies on the Case of Elder E. P. Daniels* 55).		

2. Strong drugs

Agent	Active ingredient	Uses
alcohol	alcohol	pain relief (otitis or sinusitis?)
EGW: "We were delayed one day longer than we designed. I had ague [shaking or throbbing or chills and fever] in my ear, and head was involved. I suffered much pain. Dared not be on the road. I consulted a dentist. He said the teeth were not the cause of this affliction. Then I took alcohol, sweat, and worked my best to subdue the pain, and the relief came. I am made aware that all this trouble was the result of a severe cold" (manuscript 43, 1890 [diary entry], White Estate Document—"Salamanca Vision," p. 17).		
cinchona	quinine	antiseptic, tonic, malaria, common fevers
EGW: When a returning missionary to Australia, whose son had died of malaria since his father refused to use quinine in view of the counsel in the Testimonies, asked Sister White: " 'Would I have sinned to give the boy quinine when I knew of no other way to check malaria and when the prospect was that he would die without it?' In reply she said, 'No, we are expected to do the best we can' " (W. C. White letter, Sept. 10, 1935, in 2SM 282).		
cholera mixture	several substances[2]	cholera morbus
EGW: "After [my] teeth were extracted Sister Caro shook like an aspen leaf. Her hands were shaking and she was suffering pain of body. . . . She dreaded to give pain to Sister White. She slept little Tuesday night and could scarcely eat in the morning, but she knew she must perform the operation and went through with it. Then the patient waited upon the doctor; I [Ellen White] had her seated in my easy chair and gave her sips of cholera mixture [a nostrum used for intestinal disorders]—all the stimulus I had in the house" (8MR 85).		

Agent	Active ingredient	Uses
cancer powders	several substances[3]	skin cancer

"[Brother Stephen Belden] is afflicted with a cancer. Brother Nobbs . . . has also been afflicted with what appeared to be a cancer. . . . Brother Stephen Belden has a cancer on his ear. I thought that if you would send him powders at once, with directions for their use, Brother Belden and Brother Nobbs might both be benefited by their use. Will you kindly respond by sending the powders as soon as you receive this letter?" (Ellen White to Dr. J. S. Gibbs, letter 236, 1906).

An Apparently Perplexing Problem

As one studies the remedies listed above it becomes quite evident that Ellen White herself used—and recommended for others—agents that cover the broad range of medicines, from the harmless to powerful drugs and mixtures. The inclusions came as a surprise to the author as it doubtless will to you, the reader. Is there an answer to the apparent problem? Here are some possible solutions.

1. Some may say she was inconsistent, that she said one thing and did another. But that is a most serious indictment. Apparently she herself had met such a charge, replying, "I do not preach one thing and practice another. I do not present to my hearers rules of life for them to follow while I make an exception in my own case . . . I am not guilty of drinking any tea except red-clover-top tea, and if I loved wine, tea, and coffee, I would not use these health-destroying narcotics, for I prize health and I prize a healthful example in all these things. I want to be a pattern of temperance and of good works to others" (letter 12, 1888, 2SM 302).

2. Others point out that even the biblical prophets did not always live up to the message they proclaimed. Certainly the one Balaam presented had come from God, but his lifestyle definitely did not. We might consider Miriam, Saul, and David as additional examples of God's messengers who made mistakes. While this may also be true in Ellen White's case, such a judgment should await the evaluation of other evidence.

3. Still others argue as to the proper meaning of the word "drug." To what exactly did she refer? In Edgar Caro's letter to Ellen White (see chapter 4), he quite specifically asked her what

she had in mind when she used the word "drug." Was it the poisonous remedies the medical students called "drugs," or did it include the less harmful remedies as well? Simply and clearly she answered that the drugs he referred to were the drugs she referred to. Then she explained that the simpler remedies, which are less harmful and to which he referred, were the simpler remedies to which she referred, but that these should not be used unnecessarily. Condemning a specific class of *medicinal agents*—the strong, harsh, poisonous drugs—she gave a few examples: strychnine, mercury, and opium.

4. But some will protest: "She used some of these very agents!" And she did. But hold any conclusion a few moments longer.

A Remarkable Collection of Statements

The following statements will further clarify the seeming contradiction that appears to emerge as we study the remedies table. Her statements below extended over a period of almost 40 years. Let us ponder them carefully and prayerfully. What are they telling us?

1. "Do not administer drugs. True, drugs may not be as dangerous *wisely administered* as they usually are, but in the hands of many will be hurtful to the Lord's property" (letter 3, 1884 [2SM 283; italics supplied]).

2. "There should be a careful, competent physician who will deal *scarcely ever* in drugs" (manuscript 22, 1887 [MM 139; italics supplied]).

3. "Drug medication, *as it is generally practiced*, is a curse. Educate away from drugs, use them less and less, and depend more upon hygienic agencies" (unpublished testimony 1888, subsequently published in *Healthful Living*, 1896, p. 246; italics supplied). (When she said "generally practiced" she had in mind the system of drugging that routinely administered harsh and poisonous medicines.)

4. "Thus our people, who had been taught to avoid drugs in almost every form, were receiving a different education" (letter 26a, 1889 [2SM 282]).

5. "Drugs need seldom be used" *(Health, Philanthropic, and Medical Missionary Work,* 1890, 43 [2SM 281; CH 261]).

The above three statements picture, I believe, situations in which strong drugs are to be used only rarely.

6. "Our institutions are established that the sick may be treated by hygienic methods, discarding almost entirely the use of drugs" (manuscript 44, 1896 [2SM 283; Te 88]).

Seventh-day Adventist health institutions were to encourage and support a medical practice that almost completely did away with drugs. Statements numbers 7 and 9 further support such a therapeutic approach.

7. "The use of drugs has resulted in far more harm than good, and should our physicians who claim to believe the truth, almost entirely dispense with medicine, and faithfully practice along the line of hygiene, using nature's remedies, far greater success would attend their efforts" *(Health, Philanthropic, and Medical Missionary Work,* 1896; p. 41; *The Place of Herbs in Rational Therapy,* p. 29).

8. One should not use drugs "with long names . . . until he has tried simple, natural remedies" (manuscript 45, 1898). Occasionally medical emergencies and acute illnesses might make it not possible, but in the majority of cases the physician should give the natural and less harmful agents a chance.

9. "His influence has had much to do with the abolishing of drugs to a large extent" (letter 38, 1899, in BCL 15). Here she refers to Dr. Kellogg's policy at Battle Creek Sanitarium, where he rarely administered strong drugs.

10. "The Lord would have our physicians cooperate with Him in their treatment of the sick, showing more faith and using fewer drugs. Let us rely upon God" (manuscript 14, 1904 [MM 40]). She encouraged physicians to request God's help as they viewed the needs of their patients and as they chose the best procedures and agents available to them.

A Better Understanding

Certainly such statements, made over a period of almost 40 years, leave the door slightly ajar to the occasional use of medicines or drugs. They also remove any question as to Ellen White's being in any way inconsistent to her message of drug reform, which she continued to proclaim to the time of her death. It is we who have failed to define "drugs" the way she did. We have also ignored the above counsels, which are just as inspired as those that condemn medical drug use.

To make a correct judgment regarding the apparent conflict, evidence presented in earlier chapters now comes into focus. When we carefully examine it, the apparent problem raised by the use of tea, coffee, wine, and alcohol, employed as acceptable remedies, resolves itself. The previous chapter referred to the publication *Meals Medicinal With "Herbal Simples."* Its author, Dr. Fernie, writes of treating his patients chiefly with "two simples," and lists among the simples a number of medicinal herbs that include tea and coffee. His list, interestingly, also has beverages containing alcohol and wine, agents he considered "simple remedies."

It is easy to misunderstand the broad scope of her message. Ellen White was one of the drug/health reformers, attempting to change the brutal, nonsensical manner in which orthodox medicine operated. It administered potent drugs for most any illness, minor or major. Such drugs included morphine, mercury, arsenic, strychnine, belladonna, and others. Drugging, together with bloodletting, blistering, and purging, killed the sick by the thousands. *Ellen White opposed the system of indiscriminate drugging and the practice of medicine that supported it.* Her message is clear. She was not against the occasional use of drugs for a specific recognized sickness.

Ellen White's Message and Philosophy on Drug Medication

In her writings on health and medicine she:

1. Condemned the use of harsh and poisonous drugs routinely given in large doses for long periods, especially for nonspecific reasons.

2. Condemned *the practice of medicine that focused on drug therapy* and that supported the system of drugging.

3. Urged both physicians and patients "to give nature a

chance," and to use the least harmful remedies in case of illness. Strong drugs were to be employed only rarely.

4. Urged both the physician and the patient to discard unhealthful practices.

5. Urged that *the focus of medical practice be on lifestyle change* and that physicians resort to drugs only sparingly.

Summary

While "simple remedy" can refer to agents or procedures that are physiologically harmless, it may also embrace medicinal herbs (botanic drugs, vegetable drugs) that we would have to label as "less harmful." On occasion Ellen White used or approved of remedies in the less harmful group. Only rarely did she turn to drugs from the powerful and poisonous group.

We may sum up her philosophy toward medications as follows:

1. Use natural and harmless simple remedies freely, as needed.

2. Employ simple "less harmful" remedies judiciously.

3. And only rarely turn to strong drugs.

References

[1] Categories reflecting those used in *The Cottage Physician,* a medical handbook for the home, and *The Dispensatory of the United States of America,* both books produced during Ellen White's lifetime and echoing medical thought of her time.

[2] The preparation, prepared by Sun, contains tinctures of capsicum, rhubarb (not the garden vegetable), and opium, as well as spirits of camphor and peppermint, dissolved in alcohol. Squibb marketed a somewhat similar product (*Dispensatory of the United States of America,* 20th ed., p. 1513).

[3] Unfortunately we do not have the precise name of the "powders." Of the many that existed, I list two below, perhaps the most commonly used. All contained arsenic.

Arsenical paste of Frere Come was made by mixing water with a powder consisting of 10 grains of arsenic trioxide, 40 grains of red mercuric sulphide, and 10 grains of powdered animal charcoal.

"Plunket's caustic consists of *Ranunculus acris* and *Ranunculus flammula,* each one ounce, bruised and mixed with sixty grains of arsenic trioxide and one hundred grains of sulphur; beaten into a paste and dried in the sun."

"While [arsenic trioxide] is a universal poison, the cells of unhealthy tissue are more readily affected by it than normal structure and it is therefore used widely for the destruction of *cancers,* especially of the skin. It is an ingredient of nearly all the proprietary and semi-proprietary pastes" (*Dispensatory of the United States of America,* 20th ed.), p. 195.

CHAPTER ELEVEN

A Physician Explains . . .

THE EIGHTH REMEDY

God in His love has given us the principles of both health and healing in what we commonly call "the eight natural remedies." We might illustrate them by an old-fashioned wheel with seven wooden spokes radiating out of a hub and attached at their outer ends to a rim. The hub or center is God's love, from which radiate the principles of life and healing—air, water, sunlight, exercise, rest, diet, and abstinence from harmful habits—encircled by *all-embracing trust in God's divine power.*

The reader must recognize that in the following counsels the Lord is setting forth the principles we should implement whenever possible. Ellen White recognized that when illness strikes we must care for the sick intelligently and employ all necessary means to combat the illness. She is not suggesting that we should demand that an acutely ill patient change unhealthful habits of life and expect him or her to survive just by opening the window and allowing sunshine into the room. The principles she presents are for those for whom they are applicable, taking time and condition into account. But the focus of therapy by physicians and institutional directors should be lifestyle change when and where appropriate.

Trust in Divine Power

Trust in divine power is a remedy in itself. "Pure air and water, cleanliness, a proper diet, purity of life, and a firm trust in God are remedies for the want of which thousands are dying" ([1885] 5T

443). While God is the One who heals "all our diseases," He has required humanity to play a part in the healing process. "It is not a denial of faith to use such remedies as God has provided to alleviate pain and to aid nature in her work of restoration. It is no denial of faith [for the sick who request prayer for healing] to cooperate with God, and place themselves in the condition most favorable to recovery" (2SM 286). While God works on their behalf, He also requires the sick to do what they can.

Faith and Works Together

"We do not manifest a lack of faith when we ask God to bless His remedies" (manuscript 65, 1899, 2SM 289). "Let the sick be encouraged to claim the promises of God for themselves" (manuscript 15, 1911, MM 227). From a human standpoint that is often difficult to do during times of distress, and as a consequence we put our confidence in human resources. "That which we lack in faith we make up by the use of drugs" (manuscript 169, 1902, 19MR 51). But our faith must demonstrate itself through what we do—in using the agencies that God in His love has provided. "Those who come to God in faith must cooperate with Him in accepting and using heaven-sent remedies— water, sunlight, and plenty of air" (letter 106, 1898, PC 48). She does not suggest that they are remedies for all illnesses but rather shows that we must use the agencies available. "If we neglect to do that which is within the reach of nearly every family, and ask the Lord to relieve pain when we are too indolent to make use of these remedies within our power, it is simply presumption. . . . God works and man cooperates with God" (letter 35, 1890, 2SM 297).

Here is where trust comes in. "One word from God, one touch of the divine finger, would have been enough to cure Hezekiah instantly. But instead, he was given directions to make a poultice of figs, and lay it upon the part affected. This was done, and Hezekiah was restored to health" (*ibid.* 300). "When from an enlightened conscience they [the suffering ones] do the very best they know how to do to preserve themselves in health, then in faith they may look to the Great Physician, who is a healer of the body as well as of the soul" (MM 224).

Change Unhealthful Habits

Besides utilizing in faith the heaven-sent agencies, the physician and the sufferer must do their part in bringing their own lifestyles into harmony with divine law, both physical and moral. "The grace of God is always reformatory. Every human being is in a school, where he is to learn to give up hurtful practices, and to obtain a knowledge of what he can do for himself. Those who ignore these things . . . cannot be free from disease. . . . Such people are careless, reckless, presumptuous, and self-destroying. Knowledge is strewn along their pathway, but they refuse to gather up the rays of light, saying that they depend on God. But will God do those things that He has left for them to do? Will He supply their neglect? Will He wink at their willing ignorance, and do great things for them, by restoring soul, body, and spirit, while they ignore the most simple agencies, the use of which would bring them their health? . . . Faith and works go together" (manuscript 22, 1887, MM 226).

Medical Institutions Must Support the Health Program

"Institutions for the care of the sick are to be established, where men and women suffering from disease may be placed under the care of God-fearing physicians and nurses, and be treated without drugs" (letter 305, 1905, 9T 168). "We were to have an institution where the sick could be relieved of suffering, and that without drug medication. God declared that He Himself would go before His people in this work" (GCB, Apr. 12, 1901, CH 531).

Additional statements support the concept that both the healer and the treated person must have a close and living personal relationship with God. And that while they seek God's aid, both must use those means available, which God has provided, to assist in the cooperative effort toward healing. Beyond this—the successful use of the simple, less harmful remedies—the physician must have a living faith in God's power to heal. Note the following counsel: "Therefore personal religion for all physicians in the sickroom is essential to success in giving the simple treatment without drugs" (letter 69, 1898, MM 235).

"The Lord will bless institutions conducted in accordance with His plans. He will cooperate with every physician who faithfully and conscientiously engages in this work. He will enter the rooms of the sick. He will give wisdom to the nurses" (manuscript 162, 1897, *ibid.* 229).

The Human and Divine Cooperate

"It is of no use to have seasons of prayer for the sick, while they refuse to use the simple remedies which God has provided, and which are close by them" (letter 106, 1898, PC 48). "We must cooperate with the Chief of physicians, walking in all humility of mind before Him. Then the Lord will bless our earnest efforts to relieve suffering humanity. It is not by the use of poisonous drugs that this will be done, but by the use of simple remedies" (letter 140, 1909, MM 85). "In this work the human and divine instrumentalities can cooperate in saving life, and God will add His blessing" (manuscript 162, 1897, *ibid.* 228). She cites the success of Battle Creek to encourage others. "We [Battle Creek Sanitarium workers] did not use drug concoctions; we followed hygienic methods. This work was blessed by God. It was a work in which the human instrumentality could cooperate with God in saving life" (letter 82, 1897, 2SM 293).

Special Blessing of God

"The Lord will be the helper of every physician who will work together with Him in the effort to restore suffering humanity to health, not with drugs, but with nature's remedies. Christ is the great Physician, the wonderful Healer. He gives success to those who work in partnership with Him" (letter 142, 1902, *The Place of Herbs in Rational Therapy* 18). "Many might recover without one grain of medicine, if they would live out the laws of health. Drugs need seldom be used. . . . But let fervent prayer and faith be combined with your efforts, and you will succeed" (letter 6a, 1890, MM 259, 260). "The physician should know how to pray" ([1885] 5T 443). All Adventist medical staff must bring their lives into harmony with God's laws. And the sick have a part to play, not only with their faith and prayers, but in harmonizing their lifestyle with physical and moral law.

A Commitment to Lifestyle Change

"Physicians have a work to do to bring about reform by educating the people. . . . They . . . should be taught to bring all their habits into harmony with the laws of life and health, and to discard drugs. This is a great work to be done" (letter 26a, 1889, 13MR 178). "Right and correct habits, intelligently and perseveringly practiced, will be removing the cause for disease, and the strong drugs need not be resorted to" (manuscript 22, 1897, MM 222). "Train the people to correct habits and healthful practices, remembering that an ounce of preventive is of more value than a pound of cure" (letter 17a, 1893, 2SM 280). "There is need to educate the people in right habits of living. Put no confidence in drug medicine" (letter 73a, 1896, SpM 44).

Note that she emphasized that "strong drugs need not be resorted to." She was not condemning the "simpler remedies" that are "less harmful." Such agents fall into the class of drugs in which we find caffeine, squill, or digitalis, and others discussed in the previous chapter. But the direction of therapy was to be always toward the simple and the harmless.

Cause and Effect

Illness and disease do not appear out of nowhere. "In case of sickness, the cause should be ascertained. Unhealthful conditions should be changed, wrong habits corrected" (MH 127). "The laws which God has established for the well-being of the physical structure are to be treated as divine. To every action done in violation of these laws a penalty is affixed. The transgressor is recorded as having broken the commandments of God" (manuscript 155, 1899). "The surrender of hurtful indulgences requires sacrifice. But in the end it will be found that nature, untrammeled, does her work wisely and well" (MH 127).

At times we may never determine what produced a particular illness despite a thorough examination of the patient's past and immediate lifestyle or his or her hereditary background. One must be careful about judging such cases. Biblical examples caution us about such situations. Job's friends wrongly accused him of sin, as did Christ's disciples when they demanded, "Who sinned, this man or his parents?" But when wrong habits are obvious, we must encourage others to make the necessary changes with the help of divine power.

The Power That Heals

Thus trust in divine healing, the last of the eight great natural remedies, provides a powerful agent that intertwines with and affects all of the other seven, and spills over to play an essential role in the successful use of all of the simpler and simple remedies.

Trust in divine healing requires a faith in the Great Physician and His therapeutic agencies both on the part of the sufferer and, more important, on the part of physicians. They exhibit their faith in the prayer room and on the hospital wards as they request the Divine Healer to provide wisdom, understanding, and skill. Then they are to use the agencies God has blessed.

Nurses and other medical staff must also be God-fearing and eager to do His bidding. The institutions offering such treatments are designed to support these types of healing measures, assuring them a blessing.

It is desirable that the patients also have a similar living faith in God's remedies, but regardless of their beliefs, they must cooperate with the physician in bringing their lifestyle into harmony with health-producing practices and at the same time discard all unhealthful ones.

Then, while exercising prayerful restraint, and having exploited the natural and harmless agencies, such health care still leaves open the door for the use of the less harmful remedies.

Ellen White emphasizes several points that show the role of faith in healing:

1. Prayer without using "simple remedies" is presumption (letter 35, 1890, MM 230).

2. It is also presumption to expect healing when we are too lazy to use simple remedies (2SM 297).

3. We must do the best we know how, then in faith pray to the Great Physician for Him to heal (manuscript 22, 1887, MM 224).

4. The Lord will bless institutions, cooperate with physicians, and give wisdom to nurses who work in accordance with His plans (manuscript 162, 1897, *ibid.* 229).

5. "Personal religion for all physicians in the sickroom is essential to success" in giving simple treatments without drugs (letter 69, 1898, *ibid.* 235).

One must never forget that God's infinite wisdom may overrule the pleas of the sick, the therapists, and the loved ones. We must trust Him, for He is at the very core of the eighth remedy—trust in divine healing.

Summary

The preceding counsels paint a most wondrous picture. To attempt to put it in words may be to mar it. But let us try to visualize the setting and the process envisioned.

We see in our mind's eye an institution of healing whose purpose is to support a system of therapeutics proposed by the Divine Physician Himself. It employs agents and procedures that either support the physiological functioning of the body or disrupt it as little as possible. God-fearing physicians, nurses, and other staff trustfully and prayerfully apply such measures to those who have come to them for help. Where and when appropriate, medical personnel make patients aware of their need to bring their lifestyle into harmony with physical and moral law, and that the sick must resolve, with God's help, to lay aside all unhealthful habits. It is a cooperative effort between the One who heals all our diseases, His obedient servants, and the sufferer.

Drugs with long Latin names, if they are to be used, should not be employed until—*when this is possible*—the patient has tried natural and simple remedies (see manuscript 45, 1898).

CHAPTER TWELVE

A Physician Explains . . .

THE MIGHTY PLACEBO

A Word of Explanation

The reader might rightly wonder why we introduce the topic of placebos at this point. After all, this book has been dealing with remedial agents and, to a limited extent, with the systems of medicine that deliver such things to the patient. Humanity has long recognized that the healing profession has two aspects: the *science* of medicine, and the *art* of medicine. Both play an extremely important role as to how the patient or recipient of the medicine accepts, rejects, or responds to therapy. The placebo effect operates no matter what system of medicine is involved. It is therefore extremely important that the reader understand its pervasive nature.

"The placebo leads us through the uncharted passageways of mind" and ultimately allows us to see "that the mind can carry out its difficult and wondrous missions unprompted by little pills."[1]

The Long History of Placebos

The healing profession has known about placebos for centuries. In 1628 Robert Burton wrote: "An empiric oftentimes, and a silly chirurgeon, doth more strange cures than a rational physician . . . because the patient puts his confidence in him."[2] Thomas Jefferson wrote to Dr. Casper Wistar in 1807: "One of the most successful physicians I have ever known has assured me that he used more of bread pills, drops of colored water, and powders of hickory ashes, than of all other medicines put together."[3]

"Placebo" derives from a Latin word carrying the meaning "I

shall please." Scholars believe it may have acquired its name from the desire of physicians to satisfy their patients by giving them something when the healer didn't know what to do or when the patient expected or demanded a medication.

In 1955 H. K. Beecher published his landmark paper "The Powerful Placebo."[4] Since then large numbers of studies, many using the double-blind method,[5] have provided further understanding of the remarkable phenomenon. While a few have downplayed and even denied the existence of the placebo effect,[6] the evidence favors the reality of placebos and their pervasive impact. Walter Brown in his paper "The Placebo Effect" expresses what most researchers on the subject believe: that "based on what is known, I believe that the placebo effect is a powerful part of healing and that more effort should be made to harness and enhance it."[7]

What Is a Placebo?

Traditionally the concept of a placebo has been that it is a substance that is not a drug but acts like one. Harry Boström calls a placebo "the forgotten drug."[8] Others say it is some inert preparation that looks like the real drug. It's a *sham medicine* that the patient takes, thinking it is the real thing. But a placebo is much more than medicine. Experience has shown that "placebos" can be things other than a "sham medication." A placebo is any event, idea, or agent that triggers a placebo effect. This might include a report to a patient that the test shows she does not have cancer and that her pelvic pains will disappear, planting the idea that pleasant thoughts will heal a stomach ulcer, or that wearing a copper bangle on each wrist will cure arthritis. I like the observation that "the placebo is the doctor who resides within."[9]

What Is the Placebo Effect?

Another definition states that the placebo effect is any change produced by a placebo.[10] That is, they are physiological or psychological effects occurring in an individual, usually a patient, initiated by the placebo (a sham drug); or by an agent (a person, generally a physician or therapist); or by a statement (the doctor expresses a hopeful prognosis); by a procedure (surgery, for example); or by the patient's own belief (an expectation of success). In themselves such things cannot influence the results, but they initiate a beneficial (occasionally harmful) response. Dr. A. Hróbjartsson of the University of Copenhagen considers the placebo effect "as the therapeutic change in a patient's condition that is causally connected to the patient's personal awareness of being in a clinical situation."[11] The mechanism by which the effect operates remains elusive but clearly occurs without the individual's awareness. It is known that faith in the therapist, the agent, or the expectation of success is essential. Considerable evidence shows that the physician or therapist is without doubt the most important initiator of the placebo effect.[12]

The effects of placebos duplicate those of active drugs. In general, placebos are half as effective, but sometimes equal, and occasionally exceed, the actions of the real drug. On an average 30 to 40 percent of subjects have a beneficial response to placebos.[13]

The placebo effect is real and widespread—in fact, so pervasive that it probably plays a part in most, if not all, therapies whether directed by a physician, some other therapist, a friend, or even the patient himself or herself. Many double-blind studies have observed improvement or remission and recovery in a wide variety of illnesses. They include diabetes, angina pectoris, cancers, pain (both chronic and postoperative), as well as coughs, seasickness, the nausea of pregnancy, headaches, arthritis, Parkinson's disease, and stomach ulcers.[14]

Factors That Influence the Placebo Effect

A number of factors contribute to the placebo effect. We may divide them as to how they relate to the patient, the practitioner, and the placebo itself.

The Patient. The higher the level of pain, stress, and anxiety the patient has experienced, the more favorable will be the response both to the placebo and the active drugs. Pain of short duration is more likely to be relieved than is persistent pain. The greater the anticipation and expectation of relief, together with the patient's conviction that relief is on the way, the more effective the placebo. The subject's past experience with medical and dental therapy is crucial. A favorable experience will enhance the placebo response. If unfavorable, the reverse is true: the results are negative or may even be "toxic."[15]

The duration or length of time one uses placebos is important. As the number of doses administered increases the effects grow proportionally less. Where the patient goes for therapy also plays a role. The same treatment is more effective when given in a famous institution than in an unknown one. It reflects the old adage "distant fields look greener." A therapy rendered in another country, in an exotic environment, and at a high cost, will more likely have greater benefit than when the patient receives the same treatment at home.[16]

The Practitioner. The practitioner's personal belief in and enthusiasm for his or her method of treatment, together with the way he or she recommends it to patients, is doubtless the most important factor in obtaining a positive placebo response. The power of suggestion plays a key role. The therapist's personal attitude toward the patient and that of his or her staff—receptionist, nurses, pharmacist—all affect the placebo response. When the attitudes are warm, friendly, reassuring, and relaxed, they will more likely have a positive response. And, as one might expect, a cool, irritating, preoccupied, or rejecting attitude will most likely have no beneficial effect or may trigger an undesirable reaction. Of course, a famous practitioner enhances the placebo's effectiveness.[17]

The research of many investigators has shown that it is extremely important to organize the office complex so that each component supports the patent's attending physician. The receptionist should be warm and friendly and immediately ask about the patient's well-being as he or she enters the waiting room. While registering or filling out a form the receptionist in a low confidential voice tells the patient that his or her choice was a good one, that the doctor is excellent. After the nurse calls the patient's name, he or she, too, quietly assures the patient of the doctor's competence. The physician listens attentively to the patient and speaks kindly and reassuringly. When the patient takes a prescription in to have it filled, the pharmacist, too, tells the patient that he or she went to the best physician. Such placebo treatments have produced excellent success rates.

Researchers then compared the results with the same placebos in the same office complex, with the same doctor, nurses, and other employees, but changed the scenario. When a patient arrived at the door into the waiting room the receptionist didn't even look up or give a greeting. Then as the patient approached the window or desk the receptionist appeared busy with something or other. Finally the receptionist said in a brusk manner: "What do you want?" "I have an appointment," the patient would reply. "Well then, sit down. The doctor is busy. It will be a little while." The nurse who came to call the patient was cool and curt. The physician was all business and gave the impression of being in a hurry. Even the pharmacist was aloof and distant. Such behavior virtually wiped out the placebo effect.[18]

The Placebo. We are here dealing with medications, whether botanic drugs or regular drugs. If the preparation has a unique background—came from the jungles of the Amazon, was spirited out of Hunza land or smuggled across some closed border, or was discovered by a refugee who, on his deathbed, decided to entrust the secret formula to a kind attendant—these and similar claims enhance the action of the medicine or placebo. If the agent is complex, that is, a mixture of rare substances or exotic herbs, is expensive, and has a risk associated with its use, the benefits will also increase.

The color, shape, size, odor, and taste all influence the responses of patients. Multicolored pills, tablets, or capsules work better than do small white ones. Red stimulates better than does blue. A general belief associates pink with stimulants and blue with depressants. Large pills seem more effective than small. A medicine that is pleasant-smelling and has a pleasing taste has a greater placebo action than does one with an unpleasant smell and a bad taste.[19]

When my father was about 82 years of age I would stop by most evenings on my way home from work to see how my parents were doing. One day as I entered their house my mother turned to my father and said: "Confess up! Tell Mervyn what you did." Reluctantly my dad went to the bathroom and brought back three bottles, each one shaped differently from the others. One was quart-sized; the other two would hold about a pint each. The labels on the bottles looked old-fashioned. They held vitamin and mineral supplements. My dad was explaining that a neighbor friend of his sold such preparations. The regular price was around $14 (a lot of money in the 1960s), but because Dad was a friend the price had been only $8. The tablets in the bottles were large, and those of each bottle had a different shape, color, and smell. As I recall, he was supposed to take three from the quart bottle and one from each of the smaller bottles every morning, then two from one of the smaller bottles and one from each of the other two at noon. And to finish off the day, he was to swallow two from the smaller bottle from which he had taken only one at noon, plus one from each of the remaining two bottles! Thirteen tablets each day!

I asked Dad to bring a pencil and paper. We wrote down the ingredients of each tablet from each bottle and the amount of the various vitamins and minerals present per tablet. Next we totaled the daily intake. I then suggested that Dad go to the local pharmacy the next morning and ask the pharmacist (a friend of his) for the instructions that come with each vitamin and mineral supplement (one-a-day preparations) sold by Parke-Davis, Squibb, and Lederle (all well-known pharmaceutical companies). "Tomorrow I'll stop by and we can compare the contents of the supplements of all four companies and their prices," I said.

When I arrived the next evening my father was hopping mad, sputtering about all the things he was going to do to his "friend"! The daily intake of vitamins and minerals in all four preparations were almost identical (not statistically different). Where the difference came was in the price. The average price of those sold by Parke-Davis, Squibb, and Lederle was $3.50 per 100 tablets compared to the $8 (the discounted price) Dad had paid for his 390 tablets! The total ingredients in 13 of his friend's tablets (taken daily) were virtually the same as one of the regular company's tablets (taken daily). Any positive placebo effect from his "friend's" tablets had instantly evaporated! My mother, in her quiet way, said: "Daddy [she always called my father 'Daddy'], next time don't be like Pilate. Listen to your wife's advice."

We are all susceptible to the placebo effect. One cannot characterize or distinguish those who react to placebos from those who don't. The same individual will respond one time and not react at another.[20]

Newness appeals to us. Just listen to the advertisements for toothpaste, floor polish, vacuum sweepers, and medications—new and different all the time. Sir William Osler, a famous physician of a century ago, advised his fellow practitioners: "We should use new remedies quickly, while they are still efficacious."[21]

Any specific treatment or drug (regular or botanic) may be made more effective by encouraging positive expectations. And we should remember that there is an "infinite capacity of the human mind for self-deception."[22] Some consider the placebo as "the lie that heals."[23] Plato once commented: "A lie is useful only as a medicine to men. The use of such medicine should be confined to physicians."[24]

The Situation as It Stands Today

In the 1940s, when medical research introduced the double-blind controlled study as the standard experimental method, it began to recognize the pervasiveness of the placebo phenomena in medical practice.[25] Today we acknowledge the rights of the patient in the doctor-patient relationship, raising the question as to whether this trust relationship can justify medical deception.

The Ethics of Placebo Use

Whether it is right to use placebos at all is a major discussion in itself, and though of extreme interest, the ethical problems concerning the use of placebos by healers of any type lies outside the scope of this book. I hope this short discussion on placebos and the placebo effect will provide the reader with some understanding of how widespread its effects are, and, as a result, remember to take it into proper consideration when evaluating and comparing different forms of therapy.

As we stated previously, any specific treatment or drug may be made more effective by encouraging positive expectations.[26] For this reason all who practice the healing arts or engage in the promotion or sale of agents (foods, supplements, herbs, medicinals, or even books and articles) for preserving health or healing disease, must avoid the temptation to deceive, by overstating the benefits that someone might derive from what they are doing, saying, or marketing.

"If we are to regard our patients as our moral equals and to respect their dignity as persons, we are . . . prohibited from practicing deception or manipulation on them."[27] And again: "The physician either tells or allows the patient to believe that the treatment has such potency. It is further assumed . . . that the patient's false belief in the potency of the treatment is essential for the placebo effect to occur."[28] Richard C. Cabot, an outstanding physician of a century ago, asked his peers: "Is it good for us as professional men to have our reputations rest on the expectation of not being found out?"[29]

The double-blind study, although it employs the placebo, is the best method known for evaluating any kind of drug. As long as the participants understand that some may receive a placebo, I believe its use is perfectly appropriate.

To Deceive or Not to Deceive?

Ellen White discusses the problems of what physicians should and should not disclose to their patients. She also touches on the matter of honesty. "Frankness in dealing with a patient inspires him with confidence, and thus proves an important aid to recovery. There are physicians who consider it wise policy to conceal from the patient the nature and cause of the disease from which he is suffering. Many, fearing to excite or discourage a patient by stating the truth, will hold out false hopes of recovery, and even allow a patient to go down to the grave without warning him of his danger. All this is unwise.

"It may not always be safe or best to explain to the patient the full extent of his danger. This might alarm him and retard or even prevent recovery. Nor can the whole truth always be told to those whose ailments are largely imaginary. Many of these persons are unreasonable, and have not accustomed themselves to exercise self-control. They have peculiar fancies, and imagine many things that are false in regard to themselves and to others. To them these things are real, and those who care for them need to manifest constant kindness and unwearied patience and tact.

"If these patients were told the truth in regard to themselves, some would be offended, others discouraged. Christ said to His disciples, "I have yet many things to say unto you, but ye cannot bear them now" (John 16:12). But though the truth may not all be spoken on all occasions, it is never necessary or justifiable to deceive. Never should the physician or the nurse stoop to prevarication. He who does this places himself where God cannot cooperate with him, and in forfeiting the confidence of his patients he is casting away one of the most effective human aids to their restoration.

"The power of the will is not valued as it should be. Let the will be kept awake and rightly directed, and it will impart energy to the whole being and will be a wonderful aid in the maintenance of health" (MH 245, 246).

"When the love and sympathy that Christ manifested for the sick is combined with the physician's knowledge, his very presence will be a blessing" (*ibid.* 245).

Summary

Placebos take many forms, and their effect is widespread. Usually it is positive, but occasionally it may be negative or undesirable. While the power of positive suggestion plays an important role in the healing process, and should be judiciously used, no one should exploit it for personal profit or gain or intentionally deceive another. When evaluating the effectiveness of any medicine, be it a medicinal herb, a vitamin supplement, or a regular drug, researchers must take the placebo effect into consideration. For, as Norman Cousins reminded us, "the human body is its own best apothecary and . . . the most successful prescriptions are those filled by the body itself."[30]

A Note to the Reader

The literature on the placebo and its effect is very large. Despite this, some researchers feel that our current understanding is still unsatisfactory. They describe it "rather provocatively as 'a vast, often repetitive, literature,' reflecting the fact that, 'the subject repeatedly surfaces and then sinks without a trace.'"[31] Some years ago Harry Boström, from Uppsala, Sweden, remarked in his article on placebos that "it is estimated that the British Library database contains at least 55,000 articles on the subject."[32]

References

[1] Norman Cousins, "*Anatomy of an Illness as Perceived by the Patient* (New York: W. W. Norton and Co., 1979), p. 66.

[2] Howard Brody, "The Lie That Heals: The Ethics of Giving Placebos," *Annals Int. Medicine* 97, No. 1 (July 1982): 112. *Chirurgeon* is an Old English term for "surgeon."

[3] *Ibid.*

[4] H. K. Beecher, "The Powerful Placebo," *Journal of the American Medical Association* 159, No. 17 (Dec. 24, 1955): 1602.

[5] To prevent bias a double-blind experiment requires that the principle investigator have no contact with those participating in the study. The subjects receive a medication, but do not know whether it is real or a sham (a placebo). The main researcher works with two other investigators who do not know the purpose of the study. One contacts the subject, while the other collects the data and evaluates it according to a predefined protocol or procedure. Finally they give the principal investigator the results.

[6] Gunver S. Kiene and Helmut Kiene, "Placebo Effect and Placebo Concept: A Critical Methodological and Conceptual Analysis of Reports on the Magnitude of the Placebo Effect," *Alternative Therapies in Medicine* 2, No. 6 (November 1996): 39-54.

[7] Walter A. Brown, "The Placebo Effect," *Scientific American* (January 1998): 90.

[8] Harry Broström, "Placebo—The Forgotten Drug," *Scandinavian Journal of Work Environment and Health* 23 (suppl. 3) (1997): 53-57.

[9] Cousins, p. 69.

[10] Giorgio Dobrilla and Carmelo Scarpignato, "Placebo and Placebo Effect: Their Impact on the Evaluation of Drug Response in Patients," *Digestive Diseases* 12 (1994): 369.

[11] A. Hróbjartsson, "The Uncontrollable Placebo Effect," *European Journal of Clinical Pharmacology* 50 (1996): 345.

[12] Cousins, pp. 56-58; Alfred O. Berg, "Placebo: A Brief Review for Family Physicians," *Journal of Family Practice* 5, No. 1 (1977): 97-100.

[13] Brown, p. 93.

[14] Dobrilla and Scarpignato, p. 372.

[15] Frank M. Beck, "Placebos in Dentistry: Their Profound Potential Effects," *Journal of the American Dental Association* 95 (December 1977): 1124.

[16] *Ibid.*

[17] *Ibid.*

[18] Peter S. Jensen, "The Doctor-Patient Relationship: Headed for Impasse or Improvement?" *American Internal Medicine* 95 (1981): 769.

[19] Berg, p. 99.
[20] *Ibid.*
[21] *Ibid.,* pp. 98, 99.
[22] Cousins, p. 56.
[23] Brody, p. 112.
[24] Berg, pp. 97, 98.
[25] Brody, p. 112.
[26] Berg, p. 98.
[27] Brody, p. 113.
[28] *Ibid.*
[29] *Ibid.,* p. 114.
[30] Cousins, p. 56.
[31] Hróbjartsson, p. 345.
[32] Broström, p. 55.

CHAPTER THIRTEEN

A Physician Explains . . .

SHOULD DRUGS
EVER BE USED?

An Environment for Disease

Let us, for a moment, look back at the environment in which the early pioneers of the Seventh-day Adventist Church were born. Most of the major killers at that time were the infectious diseases—diphtheria, typhoid fever, dysentery, malaria, yellow fever, and tuberculosis. All of them were rampant, some in summer and others in winter.

Beyond that, people struggled with noninfectious diseases resulting from the way they lived and the environment in which they dwelled. Garbage and human waste littered the streets, water supplies were contaminated, no rules governed the quality of food sold, and society was grossly ignorant about what to eat and how to prepare it. Houses, especially in winter, shut sunlight out and stale air in, particularly when someone in the home was ill. Such a lifestyle lowered the resistance of the population and made them more susceptible to killer diseases.

Not until the dawn of the twentieth century did medicine establish schools of public health to train physicians and other medical personnel to prevent disease. Public health authorities built sewer plants, purified the water supply, inspected food, and vaccinated against communicable diseases. Many believe today that if developing nations of the world wisely disposed of human waste, which pervasively contaminates the environment, 70 percent of the current illnesses in such countries would disappear.

How the Nineteenth Century Treated Disease

In 1850, when Ellen White was a young woman, medicine had changed little from the days of Galen. Poorly trained, with little if any understanding of physiology and pathology, with virtually no diagnostic tools, and no support from clinical laboratories and hospitals, physicians did the only thing they knew—those things doctors had done before them. They bled, purged, vomited, blistered, and drugged for almost any ailment, whether infectious or noninfectious. And the drugs they used were harsh poisonous preparations given in large doses for prolonged periods of time. Those who were already sick and suffering were thus tortured without and scoured within. The resulting death toll from medical interference was high.

As we have already discussed, medical reformers arose, each with their own new brand of medicine. Strange ideas, with no foundation based on biological knowledge or experience, gained ready acceptance. The general public, together with the medical profession, was groping. The cry of the day seemed to be that anything was better than the murderous medicine usually practiced. In the mid-1860s God looked at His own people beset with sickness and death, and in His mercy gave to Ellen White her first vision on therapeutic and health reform.

And it was indeed a remarkable message of condemnation on the one hand and encouragement on the other. She proposed a gentler, more physiological approach that used the most supportive measures to aid nature in the healing process. In addition to condemning drug medication, she urged physicians to analyze the unhealthful habits of their patients, encouraging them to change their health-destroying and disease-producing lifestyles, not alone to aid in recovery but also to prevent future illness.

What Remedies Were Available for Use?

The table on page 191 presents in outline form the remedies that we discussed earlier.

Choice of Medications		
Type	*Disease Type*	*Characteristic*[1]
natural remedies	mainly lifestyle diseases	harmless
simple remedies		
procedures	minor and major illnesses	harmless
herbs or food (harmless)	minor and major illnesses	harmless
herbs, medicinal (less harmful)	major illnesses	less harmful
drugs (powerful), regular and botanic	major illnesses	potentially harmful

You will recall that when Ellen White replied to Edgar Caro's questions about what constituted drugs she made it clear to him that she could not draw a line between which agents were completely harmless and which were harmful. The author cannot do it either, and the reader should realize that the above grouping is not inspired. I have intentionally mentioned no specific remedy. The table attempts to provide a visual grouping of remedial agents according to their type, usefulness, and characteristics.

Ellen White herself suffered many illnesses, especially in her younger years. From some of them she received miraculous healing. But with others she endured suffering and sometimes a prolonged recovery. We wish she had recorded more about the remedies she resorted to for the variety of illnesses that befell her. Below, in summary form, we list the remedies she employed or suggested.

Medications Ellen White Used or Approved[2]

1. Seasickness: coffee (1882) (2SM 302, 303); tea (regular) (1888) (*ibid.*).

2. "Tonic" or calming agent: wine (use not indicated) *Testimonies on the Case of Elder E. P. Daniels* (1888) (55).

3. Stress and anxiety: catnip tea to "quiet the nerves" (1890) (2SM 297).

4. Insomnia: hops tea (1890) (*ibid.*).

5. Pain relief: alcohol (1890) (manuscript release 1033).

6. Malaria: quinine (1890s) (2SM 282, footnote).

7. Cholera: "cholera mixture" (1893) (8MR 85).

8. Surgical procedures: anesthetics—ether, chloroform, nitrous oxide (1899) (8MR 85, 2SM 284, 285).

9. Cancer: "cancer powders" (letter 236, 1906, unreleased).

When we analyze the uses for which she employed the above-listed agents, we find she took or advocated the medicinal agents for the same conditions for which regular physicians generally prescribed them. People then regularly took coffee and tea for seasickness and vomiting, as they did hop tea for insomnia or the inability to fall asleep. Catnip tea was a standard treatment for anxiety and stress. She gave no indication why she used wine. The times commonly employed it as a tonic or as a calming agent. Her day had few pain relievers. The most frequently used were opium and alcohol. Epidemics of cholera or severe diarrheas swept the United States and Australia. The mortality was high, and medical science had no specific cure, though pharmacists sold a so-called cholera mixture (she used it in Australia). Malaria was widespread in the United States and rampant in the mission fields as well. Quinine from the bark of the cinchona tree was a specific cure for certain types of malaria. For surgical procedures the anesthetics used were chloroform and ether, both highly toxic. Nitrous oxide was more difficult to use and control. Pharmacists carried cancer powders, mainly for skin cancers. Their chief ingredient was an arsenic compound.

Of the above nine medications, the first four fall into the category we might call the "less harmful" remedies—coffee, regular tea, wine, and hops and catnip teas. They also belong to the large class of "drugs," botanic or regular, that we still commonly use today, such as caffeine, reserpine, and lanoxin. The remaining five are the more powerful drugs.

Ellen White's goal was to change the focus of the practice of medicine from the routine use of powerful and harsh drugs to more physiological remedies that were "less harmful." But she did not stop there. She warned that even these were "used when not at all necessary." Her intent was that people employ harmless physiological remedies whenever feasible, and that they, with God's blessing, would work wonders. We should not consider her a drug nihilist even though many often try to portray her as one.

As the list above shows, the agents move from the "less harmful" to the stronger medicines. We should strongly emphasize that Ellen White's maxim for treating illness and disease was (1) change unhealthful habits that may be causing the problem; and (2) regularly use harmless physiological agents and procedures; then, if the problem persists, (3) employ the "less harmful" agents judiciously, but sparingly; and finally, (4) if absolutely necessary, try the available strong remedies, but only rarely.

The author is not attempting to discuss remedies in general. Ellen White made numerous references to the use of nature's remedies and simple remedies when she came down with a cold or cough. Rather, we are attempting to focus on the use or nonuse of drugs and, in broad terms, if and when we might employ them.

The Legitimate Use of Drugs

Should the information presented above act as a model to guide in the therapeutic approach to illness and disease? Whether one likes it or not, the counsels presented are all inspired. It is apparent that *there is* a legitimate time when we can turn to the "less harmful" drugs, and, on occasion, the "harmful" ones as well. Does this allow us to use drugs freely? The answer is a resounding no! Where, then, is the rationale the Lord would have us follow? Here are a few examples of where botanic or regular drugs appear acceptable.

1. *As an adjunct to therapy.*

a. Here we would include such agents as anesthetics. Anesthetics are highly poisonous chemicals, but medical science employs them not to cure some disease, but to enable some curative procedure to be employed. Ellen White saw in vision angels standing by the side of Dr. Kellogg while he performed surgery, procedures that would employ anesthetics.

b. The use of smartweed added to the water when giving fomentations, and a bath to which some mustard has been added. Such procedures employ agents (here medicinal herbs) applied externally, in which absorption of any active ingredient is unlikely.

2. *To treat infections.*

a. Here the goal is to eradicate a foreign invader, such as a malarial parasite. In the use of quinine no attempt is made to modify some physiological system of the body, but to attack an organism.

b. Similarly, this would also include the use of drugs for the eradication of intestinal worms and parasites. The organisms are within the bowel but technically outside the body, and the medications would remain outside the body unless some absorption occurred.

c. Bearing in mind the above examples, would this include chemotherapeutic agents in general? antibiotics?

3. *To treat disorders of the skin.* Many drugs are used topically to treat skin disorders such as scabies, ringworm, and impetigo. While the majority act externally, the possibility exists that a few might be absorbed through the skin and, therefore, exert a systemic effect.

4. *To treat disorders of the eye.* This would include such diseases as glaucoma, iritis, etc.

5. *To combat allergic responses.* Here we deal with inborn and acquired sensitivities to pollens, insect stings, molds, chemicals, certain plant and animal products, etc.

6. *To counteract various problems.*

a. Endocrine deficiencies—pancreas (diabetes), thyroid, pituitary, posthysterectomy, and others.

b. Autoimmune disorders—rheumatoid arthritis, Type I diabetes, AIDS.

c. Genetic or resistant problems—hypertension (high blood pressure), hyperlipidemia (high blood cholesterol levels), osteoporosis.

d. Severe, intractable pain.

e. Severe emotional problems: psychosis, schizophrenia.

f. Severe insomnia (sleeplessness); the patient should first go to a sleep disturbance laboratory).

g. Heart problems: congestive heart failure, arrhythmias.

h. Malignancies: different types of cancer respond differently to different agents.

The list could continue. However, the examples fit the model presented above. The author has not provided representative agents for treating the various disorders, because continuing research will find less harmful or even harmless agents that will replace those in current use.

An Overview of the Counsels on Drug Use

1. While reducing drug use, employ the "less harmful" simple remedies "which will tide over" many problems (2SM 279, 290).

2. Learn to use the natural and simple remedies for the majority of your illnesses (*ibid.* 296-298).

3. Learn to live healthfully, developing a lifestyle conducive to health and in harmony with nature's laws, thus enabling you to avoid many diseases.

4. At the same time make every effort to seek means to treat disease without drugs.

5. And while we strive to overcome unhealthful habits and to live healthfully, selecting the most appropriate agents available in harmony with the Lord's counsels, prayer for God's guidance must accompany all efforts put forth for the recovery of the sick by both the physician and the patient. This could include, besides intercessory prayer, anointing by the elders of the church.

6. Then, after we have tried the natural and the harmless and less harmful simple remedies, the door remains ajar for the occasional use of strong medications.

"Without the Use of Drugs"

Medical science today understands the workings of the body and the way in which drugs affect physiological functions far better than during Ellen White's lifetime. The student of pharmacology can now see the accuracy of her description of how drugs impact the body. This growing understanding of the actions of drugs, together with the discovery of an increasing number of physiological means of treating disease during the past 75 years, provides the physician of today far greater opportunity to treat disease "without the use of drugs."

Vitamins, minerals, hormones, phytochemicals, intravenous fluids, blood, and blood constituents were either unknown or unavailable in years gone by. The greater insight into what happens during illness and the possibilities of genetic engineering[3] providing replacements for precisely what the body lacks when sick reveals the divine foresight that the time would come when medical science could treat disease "without the use of drugs."

God's counsel is sure. Let us not try to hew down Ellen White's inspired words by speaking ill-advisedly of things as yet not fully understood. Let us thank God for the remarkable advances in scientific knowledge in the areas of health and disease, and then with faith and earnest prayer do our part, trusting that He will guide in the decisions we make and bless our humble efforts to do His will.

The eight natural remedies describe the basic principles promoting a healthful lifestyle, and are useful as remedies only when we have violated them by inadequate or excessive use. Put in other terms, they are the natural remedies for an unhealthful lifestyle, and for the diseases resulting from it.

Unhealthful lifestyles are not the only reason for illness. Diseases may result from other causes, which might include infectious organisms, hereditary or genetic abnormalities, and disorders of our immune systems (autoimmune). While I cannot change my genes, God and I can change my lifestyle.

The Conclusion of the Whole Matter

In a nutshell, here is what Ellen White preached and what she practiced. *Unhealthful habits of life* overcome promptly. *Strong, poisonous drugs* used rarely. The *less harmful "drugs" in common use* utilized sparingly. *The simple and the simplest of remedies* employed freely. The *natural remedies* practiced perseveringly, and *trust in divine power* sought unceasingly.

References

[1] It is assumed that people will use the remedies with intelligence and common sense.

[2] For details see the table in chapter 9. The medications appear in chronological order.

[3] The unlocking of the secrets of the human genome (the body's complete genetic code) will open up unthought of possibilities. "The consumer will keenly feel the effects: simple blood tests, for instance, that reveal one's risk of developing cancer or Alzheimer's, or *custom-made drugs that work without side effects.* Genetic knowledge may be harnessed to cure diseases or even slow the aging process" (Leslie Roberts, "The Gene Hunters," *U.S. News & World Report*, Jan. 3-10, 2000, pp. 34-38; italics supplied).

CHAPTER FOURTEEN

A Physician Explains . . .

SOMBER REFLECTIONS

Yesterday, Today, and Tomorrow

The literature on therapeutics would fill whole libraries—it is staggering, to say the least! And unbelievably, it continues to grow at a precipitous pace. It is, in fact, flooding cyberspace! Carefully researched scientific reports pour from the laboratories of colleges and universities, along with those of commercial institutions. Then science writers popularize this technical, oftentimes heavy, information into the vernacular of the average person. This level of information attempts to be factual, but because of the process of communication it sometimes fails. And then, of course, other material promotes some commercial product. What shall we believe? Deciding is not easy.

The author has, perhaps, attempted the impossible. The reader will find that the subject dealt with in each chapter has a vast database of books and papers. To select the most factual material pertinent to the topic is no easy task. At best it must be subjective even as we attempt to be objective! Each topic covered must be incomplete, for the few references provided show how much more remains unsaid. But the author has made a studied attempt to select the most factual information and briefly express it in simple language, to allow the reader to reach a correct conclusion.

Yesterday

Ellen White's ministry spanned 1844 to 1915, some 70 years. Occupying the major portion of the latter half of the nineteenth century, it was a period of transition. The industrial revolution was well on its way. To quote Churchill: "Every morning when the world woke up, some new machinery had started running. Every night while the world had supper, it was still running."

This period, at a steadily increasing pace, laid the foundations of scientific medicine. The development of the basic sciences—the disciplines of anatomy, physiology, chemistry, microbiology, pathology, pharmacology, psychology, and others—combined with the clinical training of physicians in hospitals. Medical research was both extensive and progressive. Although the clinicians only slowly and sometimes reluctantly received the knowledge gained by the pioneers in the laboratories, the clinical practice of medicine nevertheless drastically changed.

The training of physicians (along with nurses and those in other supporting disciplines) steadily improved. It went from a preceptorship of varying length to a six-month course in the 1850s and 1860s to one or two years by 1885 and to four-year programs in the early 1900s. And it was during this time that Ellen White urged the establishment of a four-year medical school, "the very best" possible.

To support the much better trained physician, other disciplines also grew and expanded. Public health had come into its own. Improved sanitation and hygiene, with the control of human waste, the provision of pure water, the inspection of food, and immunizations against infectious diseases provided every citizen a more healthful environment.

The drugs prescribed by scientifically trained physicians began to decline in number and dangerousness for several reasons. Two stand out in particular. First, research techniques, both clinical and laboratory, found many drugs useless for the purposes prescribed, or far more dangerous than the diseases they attempted to combat. Second, medical science began to use the active principles of the herbal preparations rather than the plants themselves, allowing for careful study of the dose-response. Giving multiple agents together was on its way out. Rather than using the old shotgun approach, a medical rifle, with careful sighting, was coming into fashion. Single agents directed toward specific diseases became the new goal.

Today

From our vantage point of almost a century, let us look back for a final time at the message that Ellen White bore regarding medicinal agents. Besides attacking the system of drug medication, or drugging, the use of strong harsh powerful medicines, she urged a positive program for both physician and patient. Physicians were to change their own unhealthful habits, and were to instruct their patients to do likewise. Such a concept was almost 100 years before the medical profession and the world at large recognized that the killer diseases of the twentieth century are none other than lifestyle diseases.

Ellen White's teaching on medications was quite clear. Medical science should only *rarely* resort to the powerful drugs. The "less harmful" agents, also called drugs by the turn of the century, were to be used *sparingly* and taken only when necessary. The simple remedies, harmless when employed intelligently, would in most cases "tide one over." She advocated that people adhere to natural agencies—pure water, fresh air, sunlight, exercise, rest, a nutritious diet, and an abiding trust in divine power. The environment of the home, inside and outside, was to be clean. In addition, she encouraged personal hygiene, something not too prevalent at the time. Her program was one of reform, prevention, and intelligent medical treatment.

What do the lessons of the past teach us? It is impossible for any physician to keep pace with the ever-expanding spectrum of drugs that today's technology has produced. While physicians use single, purified agents, they often prescribe a number of drugs for the different conditions from which the patient suffers. In this way, unthinkingly, they practice "polypharmacy," the mixing taking place not in a beaker but in the body of the patient! Pressured by HMOs, insurance companies, and sometimes by their own desire for gain, the harried physician has no time to contemplate what is going on. Educate their patients in lifestyle change? Impossible. It doesn't seem cost effective! And only a very few patients ever comply.

The proliferation of proprietary remedies boggles the mind! New but just as deceptive preparations housed in capsules and tablets and available over the counter have replaced the tonics and mixtures of 100 years ago. Vitamin and mineral mixtures have been around for the past 50 years. But times are changing. Phytochemicals, biologically active compounds found in wholesome foods (just as the vitamins and minerals were) now flood the marketplace. That we need an appropriate amount of vitamins, minerals, and phytochemicals goes without saying. But people take such powerful chemicals, actually required only in minute quantities, indiscriminately in concentrated form and in enormous amounts. And now we see a rebirth in belief that the medicinal herbs of the past, in some mystical way, will provide us with health and healing. We pride ourselves on how foolish our forebears were with their unsullied faith in the nostrums of their day. But are we any different? Do we ever give thought to the possible long-term toxic effects of what we introduce into our bodies?

A Glance at the Past

Almost a century has gone since Ellen White laid down her pen and her voice was silenced. As a reformer she had a vision. What was it? We have discussed its origins and goals chapter by chapter, but what of the whole? Before we go to the future let us briefly view this past, not the details of the landscape but the broad sweep of the hills and valleys, both reaching back and looking forward to the far horizon. And what do we see?

A Large Team of Medical Reformers

Drug-health reformers were to include many others than institutional directors, physicians, nurses, and other staff members in our medical institutions and clinics. Church administrators, ministers, evangelists, colporteurs, missionaries, the staffs of our educational institutions, publishing houses, health food factories, and church members at large—each and all were to make healthful changes in their own lives, that is, adopt a healthful lifestyle, and then to encourage others to do the same. It would reduce and often eliminate the use of and need for drugs.

What a challenge! Was it ever accomplished? Only in part. But it gives us a glimpse of what might have been. As in the experience of God's people of old, they only from time to time fulfilled the plans and purposes He had for them. When they believed God's prophets and followed their counsels, they prospered. So it has been with God's people today.

A Partly Fulfilled Plan

From the vantage point of 100 years, what do we find? We see Battle Creek Sanitarium and Hospital in its heyday, an institution distinct and different from other medical institutions of its time. It had a clientele made up of the great and the powerful. The titled of Europe and the rich of the world made their way to the institution and were welcomed at its doors, as were missionaries returning from fields afar and humble church members from the towns and villages across North America. And Battle Creek treated them all with dignity and love.

Nothing else compared to it. Clones sprang up around the world. Battle Creek became a word symbolizing a mecca for the sick where the therapeutics offered were different. Under the blessing of God, it spawned the health-food industry, an industry that has changed the eating habits of the developed world: breakfast cereals and peanut-butter sandwiches, to mention just two examples.

And then disaster struck. Little by little the counsels of God went unheeded, until the day came when God's people lost the institution. Like the Temple that Solomon built, the glory that comes from God alone had vanished.

A Second Chance

But from the ashes of Battle Creek arose another medical institution that would outshine the achievements of the first. It was, as it were, a seed planted: the College of Medical Evangelists, now grown to Loma Linda University, a health-science center respected around the world. Again, whenever and wherever people have followed God's counsels, success has followed. While in practice much of its program is no different than that of other quality medical science institutions, it has become known for certain major contributions.

Dedicated medical staff, graduates of the schools of the university, have established hospitals and clinics in countries around the world. The prestige of such mission hospitals has brought to their doors the rich and the poor, the sick and the suffering. As a result doors have opened, both in the countries they have served and in the hearts of the sick, for the gospel message. For some years now the heart surgery team, organized by Doctors Wareham and Coggin, has trained medical practitioners in heart surgery in countries whose doors were shut to other missionary endeavors of the church. Only time will tell the influence engendered in countries such as Saudi Arabia, Thailand, and China.[1]

During the last decade the medical campus initiated two pioneering ventures. Under the direction of Dr. James Slater the Proton Treatment Center, the only such hospital-based accelerator in the world, was opened. Three stories high with its 250 million electron volts of radiation, the machine has proved to be a giant weapon for the treatment of cancer and certain other diseases. Dr. Leonard Bailey pioneered an infant heart-transplant program. The donor heart weighs about an ounce and takes approximately five hours to implant. His team of transplant surgeons, carrying with them appropriate equipment, obtain hearts from all over North America to save lives of babies waiting in Loma Linda.[2]

And then from the research laboratories of the university have come scientific papers that have had a significant and worldwide impact. Beginning in the early 1950s two groups of researchers began publishing in two somewhat different areas.

Drs. Lemon and Walden initiated what we now know as the Adventist Mortality Study. It later led to the Adventist Health Study, one of the longest and well-known epidemiological studies on lifestyles and their impact on wellness and disease. Their research has shown that the health habits of members of the Seventh-day Adventist Church significantly lower the risk of killer diseases such as coronary heart disease, stroke, certain types of cancer, and diabetes. And as an additional bonus, Adventists live longer than do comparable groups. Similar studies done in other countries—Norway, Denmark, and the Netherlands—have corroborated their findings.

Drs. Hardinge and Register initiated studies on nonflesh diets. They compared the diets of vegetarians with those of nonvegetarians. Their impact was gradual. The American Dietetic Association, once hostile to the concept of nonflesh diets, accepted papers on vegetarian studies beginning in the mid-1960s. In 1988 they published, with the help of Drs. Register and Zolber, a position paper accepting that vegetarian diets were adequate and wholesome. Today in the Western world nonflesh diets, once ridiculed, then tolerated, now eulogized, have increasing acceptance. Growing numbers of people have adopted them.

A Summing Up

Today the practice of medicine has changed significantly, though, with rare exceptions, it still focuses on drug therapy. When physicians examine a patient they think in terms of what medications they should prescribe, giving little thought or effort to lifestyle change.

Ellen White was a drug-health reformer. She condemned the training that physicians and nurses received and set out to reform medical education and practice, particularly the focus on drugging. Medical science should discard poisonous drugs or use them only rarely and simpler remedies or less harmful agents sparingly. Human beings must give nature a chance to heal. Natural and simple remedies were to be used to aid nature in its work, and were to be employed regularly. Ellen White urged all who could or would to adopt correct health habits themselves and teach them to those who were sick and suffering. Health education and lifestyle change were the goals of the day.

At the time living healthfully was a program to which few subscribed. People feared the night air, shut out sunlight from their homes, and only poorly understood and rarely practiced the need for personal and environmental cleanliness. Through the years, for reasons it is still difficult to understand, medical education has failed to include in its curriculum the importance of a healthy lifestyle. Today, as we have entered a new millennium, well-documented research has established beyond a doubt that unhealthy lifestyles lie at the root of most of the killer diseases seen in the developed countries of the world. But despite that, the training of physicians provides little time and only token emphasis on their obligation to evaluate the patient's lifestyle and instruct them as to why and how people should correct their unhealthful habits.

We should add that lifestyle diseases are also the major killers in the world's developing nations. Among large populations, both urban and rural, to contaminate the water and to contaminate the soil from human wastes is almost a way of life, increasing the incidence of and mortality from infectious diseases.

Today the practice of medicine, with rare exceptions, still focuses on drug therapy. When physicians examine a patient they think in terms of what medications they should prescribe, giving little thought or effort to lifestyle change.

Have We Largely Missed the Boat?

Tomorrow could be just another day—like today. But it does not have to be. We can make a change, can make it different. We now have an improved understanding of humanity as a whole. Our genetic background determines, in part, the diseases to which we are heir. But we also realize that a healthy way of life will promote well-being, reduce the incidence and severity of a number of serious diseases, prolong life, and improve its quality.

What more potent preventives can be found than appropriate exercise, pure water, sunlight and fresh air, relaxation, rest and sound sleep, nutritious food for body and mind, and abiding trust in divine power and supervision? They have no side effects!

And then, if after we have done all we can to stay well, because of the frailty of nature, illness may still strike. But our past healthy lifestyle will greatly increase our chances for survival. And to aid us at such times, our Creator has provided and blessed intelligently prescribed remedies.

Ringing down the centuries one can hear the words:

"These you ought to have done, without leaving the others undone" (Matt. 23:23, NKJV).

"Believe in the Lord your God, and you shall be established; believe His prophets, and you shall prosper" (2 Chron. 20:20, NKJV).

References

[1] Richard Shaefer, "An Enterprise That Has No Future," *Alumni Journal,* School of Medicine, Loma Linda University, vol. 71, No. 4, p. 12.

[2] "The Medical Center and University have become international institutions. Their 3,250 students come from 85 countries. Their 9,700 employees come from 100 countries. They speak 40 languages. Loma Linda University Medical Center is today the flagship of the worldwide Seventh-day Adventist health-care service, which reaches into 75 countries and employs 76,000 people in 650 medical institutions. It has been recognized by *U.S. News and World Report* as one of "the best hospitals in America." The Loma Linda University School of Medicine has now graduated 8,283 physicians. It has graduated more physicians who have become medical missionaries than has any other school of medicine in the world" (*ibid.* pp. 12, 13).

GLOSSARY

Aconite: The active ingredient obtained from the root of Monkshood (*Aconitum napellus*), and used as a sedative and an anodyne (to reduce fever). Used as a syrup. Toxic levels weaken the heart, slow respiration, and produce sedation, stupor, convulsions, and death.

Adenitis: Inflammation of a gland, especially the lymph nodes in the neck (lymphadenitis).

Alum: Either potassium or ammonium aluminum sulfate employed as an emetic (vomiting agent), astringent (coagulates mucus), or styptic (used to stop bleeding).

Alvine: Related to the intestines.

Antibiotic: A substance produced by or partially derived from a microorganism used to inhibit or kill another microorganism.

Antimony: An emetic (vomiting agent) usually used in the form of tartar emetic.

Apothecary: A person who compounds or puts various ingredients together as a medicine or who prepares and sells medicines (drugs).

Apprentice: A person who agrees to work with another individual for a specified period of time in order to learn a profession or trade.

Arsenic: A poisonous element that in one or another chemical form was at one time used as a medicine.

Astringents: Substances used to thicken, or coagulate, or decrease mucous secretions.

Ataxia: See Locomotor ataxia.

Atheroma: A fatty degeneration or a fatty deposit in the wall of an artery.

Atropine: A poisonous alkaloid obtained from the belladonna and other plants (family *Solanaceae*) used to decrease secretions, dilate the pupil of the eye, and relieve spasms.

Bark: Usually refers to cinchona bark, the source of quinine and other alkaloids, including quinidine. Effective in treating certain forms of malaria. Also known as Peruvian bark or Jesuit's bark. Because of its bitter taste often added to certain drinks, called bitters, or bitter tonics.

Belladonna: A medicinal extract of the nightshade plant containing atropine. The plant is often referred to as the deadly nightshade.

Blister: A raised area of the skin filled with liquid.

Bonesetter: An unlicensed person who realigns dislocated or broken bones.

Calabar bean: The highly poisonous seeds of the vine *Physostigma venenosum* Balflour, at one time used by the natives of West Africa as a means of "trial by ordeal" for witchcraft. Physostigmine, the active alkaloid in the calabar bean, stimulates the salivary glands and the mucous secreting glands in the trachea, bronchi, and bronchioles. The outpouring of saliva and mucous is extreme. The suspected guilty party eats calabar beans. If the person drowned in his own secretions, he or she was guilty, but if the person survived, he or she was innocent. In medicine, it was employed as a powder to relieve constipation and to sedate the spinal cord. Today, physostigmine, or one of its derivatives, is one of the agents used in the treatment of glaucoma.

Calamy: A fluid-extract made from the root of the sweet flag *(Aconus calamus)*. Has a pungent, aromatic taste. Used to relieve pain as well as uneasiness of the stomach and bowels.

Calcareous: Deposits containing calcium or calcium carbonate.

Calomel: A compound of mercury, mercury bichloride, widely used in the nineteenth century as a purgative.

Camphor: A gummy poisonous substance, but with a pleasant odor, obtained from the wood and bark of the camphor tree, and at one time employed in medicine as a sweating agent, a general sedative, a heart stimulant, an antispasmodic to relieve colic, and for certain diarrheas. Although no longer used internally, it still appears in certain liniments for its fragrance and cooling properties.

Cannabis sativa: Also hemp, hashish, or marijuana. People smoke marijuana for its psychoactive properties. It changes mood, perception, and motivation, producing a "high." Generally its effect lasts about two hours, during which perception, reaction time, memory, and learning remain impaired. Coordination stays damaged for a longer period.

Cantharides: A preparation of ground-up beetles (Spanish flies) used formerly as an irritant, producing blisters on the skin, and internally as an aphrodisiac.

Carminative: An agent that relieves colic or griping with or without the release of gas.

Cataplasm: An older term for a poultice. See Poultice.

Catechu: An astringent obtained from the twigs and leaves of the gambier plant. Used in the treatment of diarrheas.

Catharsis: To cleanse or purge. Commonly refers to the response of medicines (cathartics) that evacuate the colon (bowel movements). May also indicate emotional cleansing.

CAT scan: Computerized axial tomography, a three-dimensional image of the internal structures of the body made by means of X-rays of sequential sections of the body (or any part) integrated by a computer.

Cirrhosis: The growth of fibrous tissue within the liver resulting in the formation of nodules of liver cells, causing hardening of the organ and disrupting its function.

Club-moss: Generally indicates the spores of *Lycopodium clavatum.* Used as a powder to sooth irritated skin. People once considered the plant itself to be a diuretic and antispasmodic, and it was prescribed for rheumatism and for diseases of the lungs and kidneys.

Colocynth (bitter apple, bitter cucumber, bitter gourd): A vine whose fruit contains a bitter yellow glucoside, colocynthin, formerly used as a powerful or drastic cathartic.

Consumption: Formerly a common term for tuberculosis.

Consumptive: A person who has tuberculosis or consumption, a wasting disease caused by a germ (*Mycobacterium tuberculosis*), and usually referring to an infection of the lungs.

Convulsant: Any substance that will induce convulsions.

Croton oil: Obtained from the seeds of *Croton tiglium,* a small tree or shrub. Formerly used as a drastic purgative in obstinate constipation, causing speedy purging. Apt to cause vomiting, severe cramping, bleeding, and sometimes death. Applied to the skin it produces redness and blistering.

Cupping: A method of withdrawing blood from the skin by applying a cup or glass from which the air has been removed, forming a vacuum. If the skin is left intact, it is called *dry* cupping. But if the physician cuts the skin with a lancet or scarificator it is termed *wet* cupping.

Diabetes: Usually refers to diabetes mellitus as a result of an inadequate secretion or utilization of insulin resulting in abnormally high levels of sugar (glucose) in the blood and urine. Onset: Type I usually in children; Type II typically in adults.

Dover's powder: A powder consisting of opium and ipecac used as a sedative and sweating agent. Formerly employed in the treatment of influenza and the common cold.

Drastic: A drug whose action is rapid and violent. The term *drastics* applied to a number of drugs whose actions were severe. Commonly indicates purgatives or cathartics.

Dropsy: See Edema.

Dulcamara, or bittersweet: *Solanum dulcamara,* named bittersweet because at first it tastes bitter, then sweet. Used as a diuretic and sedative, but especially for scaly skin lesions, such as psoriasis.

Debility: General weakness.

Degeneration: Deterioration of tissues or organs with loss of function, strength, and vitality.

Diaphoretic: An agent able to cause profuse sweating.

Diarrhea: Abnormally frequent discharge of stools, usually watery.

Digestant: An agent that aids digestion.

Eclectic: In medicine, one who believes in selecting for use only the best of medicinal agents. Those who practiced this form of medicine were called eclectics.

Edema: Accumulation of fluid in the tissues of the body; more commonly collecting in the lower body and limbs.

Electrocardiogram: A tracing made of the changing electrical activity of the heart during a heartbeat.

Electrograph: A machine that measures the changing electrical activity in the heart muscle during a contraction or heartbeat and records the changes in the form of a tracing electrocardiogram.

Emetic: A drug that initiates vomiting.

Emmenagogue: A drug that acts on the uterus promoting menstrual discharge.

Epsom salts: Hydrated magnesium sulfate used as a cathartic.

Euphorbium: A yellow-brown resin obtained from *Euphorbia resinifera*; its taste at first mild, then acrid and burning. Formerly used as an emetic and cathartic. Because of its harsh action later used only externally as a rubefacient (producing redness).

Excitant: A stimulant that arouses or excites the functions of one or more organs or systems.

Expectorant: A substance that causes the discharge of mucus and other matter from the throat, trachea, and lungs.

Expectorate or expectoration: The act of discharging material from the throat, trachea, and lungs.

Fibroid: A nonmalignant fibrous mass occurring in the muscular wall of the uterus.

Fluidextract: A concentrated solution of a vegetable drug employing alcohol as a solvent or preservative, and containing the active constituents of one gram of dry drug in each milliliter of fluid.

Gall: A somewhat rounded structure formed on the smaller branches of certain oaks and certain other plants from an injury by a fungus or insect, providing a source of tannin or tannic acid. Possesses a strong bitter taste. Formerly used as an astringent. Also an old term for bile.

Hardtack: A dry hard saltless biscuit provided by the British Navy as part of the food ration for their sailors.

Hellebore, swamp, or veratrum or Indian poke: A brownish gray powder obtained from the tissues of the hellebore *(Veratrum viride* or *Veratrum album)*. Administered as a powder, it is a powerful depressant of the heart and spinal nerves. It is also a powerful emetic and cathartic. An overdose causes death by cardiac arrest.

Hemlock: Contains conium, a highly toxic substance causing convulsions and death.

Hepatic dysfunction: A general term implying a poorly functioning liver.

Hormone: A substance produced by a group of specialized cells, transported by the blood or other body fluids, and effecting the actions of cells remote from its origin.

Horseradish: The ground-up root of a plant of the mustard family *(Cochlearia armoracia)*. Commonly used as a condiment. Formerly used only in the fresh state as a digestant, diuretic, and externally as a rubefacient.

Hydrocyanic acid or hydrogen cyanide: An extremely poisonous substance, once used in the treatment of whooping cough.

Indian poke: See Hellebore.

Infusion: Refers to the water in which a medicinal herb has been steeped. A tea. Also the process of introducing a solution into body tissues, most commonly, a vein.

Interstitial: Applying to tissues, usually fibrous, inside an organ or structure.

Ipecac or Ipecacuanha: The active ingredient emetine obtained from the dried roots and rhizome of the plants *Cephaelis acuminata* and *Cephaelis ipecacuanha*, given as a syrup to cause vomiting.

Jaborandi or philocarpus: The leaflets of the woody shrub *Pilocarpus jaborandi* contain the alkaloid pilocarpine. A crude of the syrup was employed as a diaphoretic (to cause sweating), in hypertension, in jaundice, and by ophthalmologists as a myotic.

Jalap: Obtained from the resinous powdered root of the plant *Ipomoea purga,* jalap, a glucoside, acts as a drastic purgative.

Kino: An astringent obtained from the bark of a number of tropical trees. Used in diarrheas.

Krameria root: See Rhatany.

Lancinating: Piercing or stabbing sensations of pain.

Larynx: The upper end of the trachea or voice box containing the vocal cords.

Laudanum: A tincture of opium containing, among other alkaloids, morphine and codeine.

Lead acetate: Also called "sugar of lead." Used to soothe the irritated intestinal lining (mucosa) in certain diarrheas.

Leeching: To bleed or withdraw blood by the aid of leeches.

Licorice: The dried root of the plant *Glycyrrhiza glabra,* used, in a dry form or as an extract, as a laxative, as a diuretic, and in sore throats, coughs, bronchitis, and peptic ulcers. Overdosage causes hypertension, heart problems, and edema.

Liniment: A preparation, liquid or semiliquid, applied to the skin to soothe or relieve pain, or one that acts as a counterirritant to cause superficial inflammation.

Locomotor ataxia: Also known as *Tabes dorsalis,* an advanced stage of syphilis affecting the nervous system, especially the spinal cord, with loss of coordination (difficulty in standing or walking), and problems with sensation, pain, vision, and nutrition, leading to wasting.

Lycopodium or club moss: See under Club moss.

Marijuana: See *Cannabis sativa.*

Marsh tea, ledum, or wild rosemary *(Ledum palustre):* A small evergreen shrub growing in swampy areas, its leaves once believed to be narcotic and diaphoretic. Used in dysentery and skin infections such as leprosy and scabies. The leaves have an agreeable odor and taste, and it is reported that during the American Revolution many drank it as a substitute for tea.

Mattioli, antidote of: Another name for theriac.

Microbiology: A specialty dealing with microscopic organisms.

Miliary tuberculosis: See Tuberculosis.

Mixtures: One or more medicines mixed together and prescribed in powder or liquid form.

Morbid: A wasting illness with a prognosis of impending death. An unhealthy attitude with forebodings of gloom, depression, and despair.

Mustard plasters: A paste containing mustard applied to the skin causing redness, irritation, and blisters.

Nauseant: Any substance that causes vomiting.

Nephritis: Infection of the kidneys.

Neuralgia: Sharp, periodic pain that follows the path of one or more apparently normal nerves.

Neurasthenia: A psychological and emotional condition exhibiting fatigue, lack of motivation, loss of interest, lack of zest, feelings of inadequacy, accompanied with problems of digestion and circulation.

Neurotic: Formerly a toxic agent that affects the nervous system. A person with a mental and emotional disorder associated with anxieties and phobias with varying symptoms that come and go.

Neurotransmitter: A substance, often a hormone, that transmits a nerve impulse from one nerve to another or one neuron to another.

Opium: The dried juice from the head of the opium poppy *(Papaver somniferum)*, the raw material providing the source of the alkaloids codeine and morphine. Both are pain relieving but highly addictive.

Paroxysm: An abrupt onset of symptoms, sometimes referred to as a fit or an attack.

Peruvian bark or bark: The bark of a South American tree *(Cinchona ledgeriana)* formerly employed for fevers, especially malaria. The source of the alkaloids quinine, used for malaria, and quinidine, a treatment for certain cardiac problems.

Phagocyte: A scavenger cell that devours foreign materials, such as germs and tissue debris.

Pharmacology: The science of understanding the properties and reactions of drugs.

Pharmacy: The art of preparing and dispensing drugs and other medicinal preparations. Today, includes counseling regarding their choice and use.

Podophyllum: The dried rootlets and rhizome of the mayapple *(Podophyllum peltatum),* formerly used as a drastic cathartic and as a cholagogue (to increase the flow of bile).

Poultice: A soft heated mass spread on a cloth and placed on an infection (boil, sore), or over a lesion deep to the skin. The material employed varies widely (examples: moistened bread, cooked rice, clay) and is sometimes medicated.

Powders: A mixture of two or more medicines reduced to finely ground particles.

Preceptor: A practicing physician who personally trains a medical student.

Purgatives: Usually refers to powerful cathartics that cause repeated evacuations of the bowels, often with watery or sometimes bloody stools.

Purge: To clean out the bowels, usually by means of a harsh medicine.

Quinine: See Cinchona bark.

Remittent: An illness whose symptoms alternatively appear and disappear.

Rhatany or Peruvian rhatany: A powerful astringent obtained from the krameria root *(Krameria triandra)* and the roots of other shrubs of the same genus. Used in the treatment of diarrheas.

Rheumatism: A condition in which the sufferer experiences stiffness and pain in muscles and joints, especially during motion. Of more recent time, rheumatic fever or rheumatoid arthritis.

Rhubarb: Not to be mistaken for the common rhubarb used for a food. Rhubarb, the vegetable drug, derives from a number of plants of the genus *Rheum* whose roots and rhizomes are employed as a purgative, and as a stimulant or tonic to the stomach (a stomachic).

Rubefacient: A substance producing redness when applied to the skin.

Sabadilla: A Mexican lily *(Schoenocaulon officinalis)* whose seeds provide the alkaloid veratrine. Formerly used to lower blood pressure and cause vomiting. May be found in insecticides. See under Hellebore.

Scarificator: An instrument consisting of a number of lancets, activated by a spring, for cutting the skin prior to cupping.

Sciatica: Specifically, pain traveling along the sciatic nerve. Generally refers to pain in the lower back, back of the hips, and thigh.

Sclerosis: Hardening caused by overgrowth of fibrous tissue. Formerly applied to any disease involving sclerosis. More specifically to patchy degeneration of the spinal cord and brain resulting in paralysis, tremors, headaches, etc., or multiple sclerosis.

Scoparius: Scotch broom *(Cytisus scoparius),* whose dried heads yield the alkaloid sparteine. Prescribed as a tea for irregular heart beat and as a diuretic. Its dried tops also serve as a diuretic.

Scurvy: A disease resulting from a deficiency of vitamin C, causing swollen friable gums, loosening of the teeth, and bleeding under the skin and mucous membranes.

Senega or seneca snakeroot: A tea, fluidextract, or tincture made from the plant *Polygala senega* and used for bronchitis and asthma. Large doses cause violent vomiting and purging. The Indians of North America took it for earaches.

Sphygmomanometer: An instrument used to measure the arterial blood pressure.

Squill: The inner scales of the bulb of a perennial plant *(Urginea maritima)* used as a fluidextract or tincture for chronic heart disease with dropsy, and also as a diuretic in cirrhosis of the liver. Possess glucosides with digitalislike properties.

Staphysagria (Stavesacre): A delphinium *(Delphinium staphisagria)* whose seeds formerly provided an emetic and cathartic. Found to be too violent. Also used in neuralgia, rheumatism, and paralysis.

Stethoscope: An instrument designed to allow one to hear the sounds produced within the body.

Sweet spirits of niter: An alcoholic solution of sodium nitrite that when inhaled causes increased pulse rate and sweating. Used as a diaphoretic (sweating agent) in fevers.

Tannic acid: An astringent. Coagulates mucus and used in diarrheas in the hope of coating the irritated intestinal wall.

Tartar emetic: A efflorescent poisonous salt (antimony potassium tartrate) with a metallic taste, at one time used as an emetic and as a diaphoretic (sweating agent). More recently employed for amebic dysentery.

Temporal: Relating to the area covering the temporal bone on either side of the skull and lying behind, above, and in front of the ear. Often referred to as the temple.

Theriac: A mixture of medicinal herbs together; a variety of animal and plant tissues originally concocted by a famous Greek physician, Galen. Its ingredients grew in numbers through the years from some 70 to more than 200 by the 1800s.

Tincture: A solution of a medicinal preparation in alcohol, usually expressed in percent: 5 percent, 8 percent, 10 percent, and so on.

Tonics: A preparation containing an agent or agents (drugs, vitamins, or herbs) believed to restore physical and mental vigor, and that refreshes and invigorates.

Tuberculosis, miliary: When the bacilli causing tuberculosis have become widespread in the body and have formed clusters of infection (tubercles) in the tissues.

Vehicle: A liquid, such as water, alcohol, honey, or sugar syrup, into which extracts of medicinal herbs, drugs, or other substances are mixed, in order to provide a means of administrating the medicine.

Veratrum: See Hellebore.

INDEX